To
Ora R. Vick
Merry Christmas
and all good wishes of
Herb Block

HERBLOCK'S
Special for Today

BY HERBERT BLOCK

SIMON AND SCHUSTER

NEW YORK · 1958

LIBRARY OF CONGRESS CATALOG CARD NUMBER: 58-13755

MANUFACTURED IN THE UNITED STATES OF AMERICA
BY AMERICAN BOOK—STRATFORD PRESS, INC., NEW YORK

Once more to my brother Bill—WILLIAM J. BLOCK—who got me into journalism. He was, as the Chicago *Sun-Times* wrote in an editorial about him, "beloved and respected" and "one of the best reporters in Chicago's newspaper history." In any place he'd have been one of the best in history and one of the most liked. There was no better newspaperman, no nicer or more generous guy, no one who was more fun to be with.

Contents

"Well, We Certainly Botched This Job. What'll We Stamp It—
'Secret' Or 'Top Secret'?"

1

INFORMATION PLEASE, DAMMIT

A QUESTION that keeps coming up from time to time, and from era to era, is "What will history say about what's happening these days?" That history business is always pretty iffy stuff, because it depends a good deal on who the historians are. And since the development of nuclear bombs, there's even a certain iffiness about whether there'll *be* historians—or whether they'll be close enough to this period to get the drift of things.

If they are thousands and thousands of years away, they may never get us figured out at all. After a few centuries of digging, they might decipher some English-language equivalent of the Rosetta stone, shout "Eureka!" and figure they had the key to understanding us. But just when they thought they could translate everything, they'd come across some government regulations or the transcript of a White House press conference. Then they'd get discouraged, throw up their hands, and go back to studying cave paintings.

But even if the historians don't have to piece together a blasted planet, they're still going to have quite a job piecing together the story of our times.

There's going to be a tremendous mass of radio and TV tapes to go through, even after they've filtered out all the commercials—which need more filtering, YES, *more* filtering than any other commercials! (No other period in history can make that claim.)

And then there will be the mountains of printed matter to be sifted for significant items. Some time-saving historian will probably try to do a quickie job based on old issues of something calling itself a weekly newsmagazine, because it's printed on good glossy stock and the pages ought to hold up well even if the articles printed on them don't. He's going to have a terrible time trying to separate fact from fancy and political opinion—and an even worse time figuring what facts have been chopped in half or left out completely. He'll end up abandoning the whole thing and writing plain, honest fiction, which will be much better for everybody.

But even the fellows who work patiently on straight factual material are going to find a lot of things confusing—I mean even beyond such obviously baffling stuff as rock 'n' roll and women's fashions.

In studying our national and international affairs, they're likely to be struck by the paradox of how we could have been so frightened and so complacent, both at the same time.

Then, while they're reading about the development of nuclear bombs and rockets, they'll find, right in the middle of all that, eruptions of a "racial issue." And they'll wonder how there could have been any question about race except survival of the human race.

They'll compare the high-sounding speeches of some of our politicians with their performances in office and they'll figure there's quite a gap there. And they'll be right.

If things go badly here, they're going to wonder how the world caved in on us while we were sitting on top of it. And if we muddle through, they're still likely to find it curious that as we developed wider and wider means of communication, we seemed to have less and less to communicate to each other.

They'll find endless speeches about freedom, and perhaps they'll wonder just what we *did* with all that freedom—or how many of the people who talked about it even knew what it was.

I think the one thing they're pretty sure to say is that it's a pity we didn't have better information, and strange that we didn't have more of it under a great democratic government.

Of course the historians will have a great advantage over us in studying this period. If they are far enough in the future, they'll see a lot of official material that we don't have access to. The government has already "declassified" quite a few documents on the Revolutionary War, and in a few more centuries they will probably make available some of the piled-up information about our present-day affairs. They will, that is, unless all this material is first declassified by exploding missiles.

The House Government Operations Subcommittee, headed by Congressman John Moss, has had quite a job just trying to find out how much government information is hidden, but it has given us a pretty good idea of what's stashed away. It has reported that over a million people in government—civilian and military—are authorized to wield secrecy stamps; and that federal documents concealed through the use of these stamps would fill a file drawer 575 miles long.

The estimate of centuries for declassification of this stuff is probably on the modest side. Even if government officials were willing to co-operate, our population could hardly supply the skilled manpower needed to separate the few legitimate secrets from all the material which is merely labeled secret. And it takes much longer to read and judge documents than it does to stamp them "confidential" and stick them in files.

Through the efforts of the Moss Committee we have also had some revealing glimpses of the kind of secrets which fill those 575 miles of drawer space. These have included such exciting documents as a report on bows and arrows, and another on man-eating sharks, which itself included excerpts from a 1916 magazine article on the subject. One can only speculate whether these secret files might also contain some stale sandwiches which government employees of bygone days might have brought to the office wrapped in old newspapers, which were promptly stamped "secret" and locked up. Somewhere in those files, there might also be a yellow-page telephone directory carefully sealed away because its cover carried the word "classified."

Lest anyone think such possibilities are too ridiculous, consider the fact

"On This Order For A New Typewriter Ribbon—Did You Know You Forgot To Stamp It 'Secret'?"

"It's A Great Performance Going On— Take My Word For It"

7/25/56

11/19/56

that a volume of public speeches was recently found to have been given the "security" treatment. And then there was the weather report which could be obtained by anyone who dialed a number prominently listed in the Pentagon phone book. The weather announcement, repeated continuously, was followed by the warning, also repeated over and over, that the information the listener had just heard was classified and was for the ears of authorized personnel only. If that kind of stuff had been slipped to some unauthorized listener, he'd have been getting some real outside dope.

There is a certain method to the madness which slaps secrecy labels on general information, and it was explained to the Moss Committee by a Defense Department official in charge of declassification policy. He said that an official can get into serious trouble for underclassifying a secret, but "I have never known a man (in our 180 years of history) to be court-martialed for overclassifying a paper."

Nothing could better illustrate the manner in which such a system of secrecy creates more concern for job security than it does for the national security.

Unfortunately, the withholding of information goes far beyond the foolish locking up of papers about bows and arrows. It also conceals knowledge of life-and-death importance to us about the effects of more modern weapons.

Early information on the area and intensity of nuclear fallout, for example, was not made available in our own country till well after it was widely known abroad. This secret was so well kept—from us—that when it finally became public, even Civilian Defense officials were caught with their plans down and suddenly found that their previous work had been practically useless.

There have been enough cases of information known to other countries— including potential aggressors—but withheld from the American people, to make one wonder who our officials regard as the enemy. Or to make us ask some of them, in the words of Mr. Roberts in the play of the same name, "How did you get on our side?"

One group which Administration officials have seemed to regard with distrust, if not hostility, has been the scientists. These men, who now comprise our first line of defense, have been so compartmentalized and so thoroughly fouled up by security procedures that they have often lacked access to information necessary in their work. The attitude toward them has seemed to be: "Sh! Don't ask. You might be a spy."

Lewis Strauss, when he was Chairman of what I sometimes labeled The Atomic Energy Good News Commission, took a particularly dim view of scientists who declined to talk happy talk and who did not join him in urging us to keep smiling till the mushroom-shaped clouds rolled by. From the way the AEC kept pooh-poohing the possible effects of nuclear radiation, it

"Look, Lady—You Don't See Me Worrying"

4/30/57

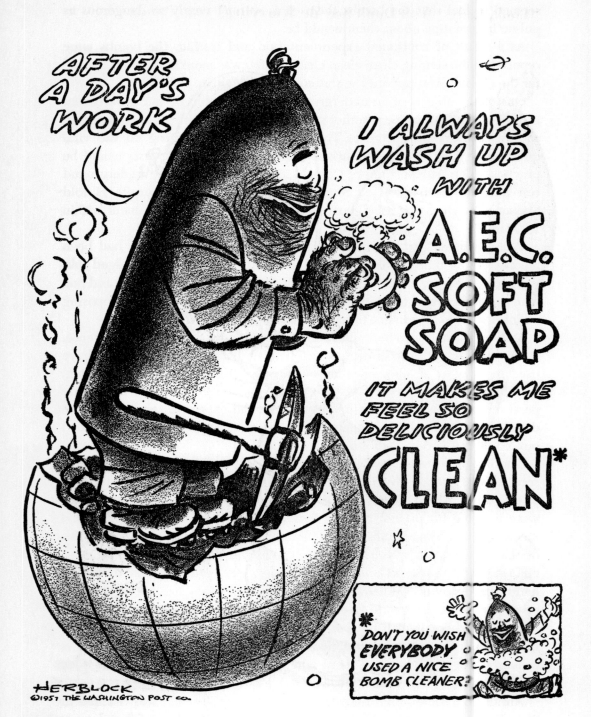

seemed to feel that the bombs themselves weren't nearly so dangerous as public information about them would be.

As a result of continued experimentation and testing, the bombs were reported to be coming clean clean clean, which was more than could be said for the officials who put out the statements about them.

One of the objects of an underground test conducted by our government in 1957 was to determine whether such a "concealed" shot could be detected at any considerable distance. This had an obvious bearing on the vital question of whether an international agreement to suspend tests would be practical. The Atomic Energy Commission reported that the underground test had not been detected more than 250 miles away—despite Harold Stassen's assertion that it had been noted on every seismic instrument within 1,000 miles.

When Senator Hubert Humphrey revealed that the explosion had been recorded more than 2,300 miles away, the AEC blandly acknowledged that its report had been erroneous. This was a slight error of 2,000 miles, and one which just happened to be in favor of the AEC Chairman's policy of opposing an international agreement to ban nuclear tests.

Secrecy has not been limited to matters involving our survival and defense. It has run through the entire government, and many public officials have used security as an all-concealing cloak to keep their slips from showing.

It took the combined efforts of many members of Congress and many persistent newspapermen to pry loose from the executive department the details of the Dixon-Yates electric-power negotiations—which, as it turned out, could not survive exposure.

Another of many interesting examples of what might be called political security was revealed by Senator Kefauver in the course of an investigation of oil prices. About a year and a half before several major oil companies were indicted for price-fixing, the Senator discovered the record of a 1956 meeting of government officials and oil industry representatives. The minutes of that meeting, in which the oil men told the unprotesting government officials that if the Suez Canal was closed they were going to boost oil prices, had been "classified." When the Senator asked why they had been classified, no one was able to provide an answer.

In cases where officials have used their secrecy stamps to keep such information from the voters, it is difficult to avoid the impression that quiet is requested for the benefit of those who do not wish to retire. The obvious theory operating here is that what we don't know won't hurt *them*.

An all-time something in government secrecy foolishness was reached in State Department instructions to personnel. In 1958, members of that department were instructed that in speaking with newsmen, they should be accompanied by public-relations officers. Earlier instructions had warned against

"Are You Daring To Make The Fantastic Suggestion That I've Been Keeping An Elephant In My Room?"

9/9/56

"... He Wasn't There Again Today. Oh, How I Wish He'd Go Away"

9/12/55

"Don't Say I'm Not A Good Watchman— I Watched The Whole Thing"

2/12/57

Report From Behind The Golden Curtain

3/10/57

16

answering even "such apparently innocuous questions as 'What is the capital of Paraguay?' " because these might lead to other questions on more delicate subjects. It's easy to see how that could happen. If a reporter started out asking what was the capital of Paraguay, he might gradually work up to asking what's the capital of the United States. And then—boom—next thing you know, he'd be asking, "Say, what kind of government have we got there now, anyhow?" That could be a pretty hard question to answer.

The real super-duper government secret is the answer to the question, What's all the secrecy about? President Eisenhower once commented that he couldn't think of a single government secret that hadn't already been printed in the newspapers. Such an off-the-cuff remark needn't be taken too literally. But it might very well be said that there are darn few government secrets that might not just as well—might much better, in fact—be printed in our newspapers. And some distinguished scientists have testified that we would quite possibly be further ahead in government science without any secrecy-security regulations at all.

The "right to know," which many papers have referred to, is not just an idle phrase. Basically the security of a free country like ours depends not upon how much can be kept secret but upon how much can be made known to the people.

In the Will Rogers movie version of *A Connecticut Yankee in King Arthur's Court*, there was a delightful line which spoofed the humorist's favorite phrase. Pointing to Will Rogers, one knight muttered to another, "All he knoweth is what he readeth in the papers; and all he readeth is what he writeth himself."

Of expedient government officials who are hipped on secrecy, it might be said that all they do is based on what they hear from the people, and all they hear from the people is based on what they tell the people themselves.

But our government was not designed to operate in an echo chamber; and nobody shows much leadership on a merry-go-round.

J. R. Wiggins, former chairman of the Freedom of Information Committee of the American Society of Newspaper Editors, said in a 1958 speech on Secrecy, Security and Freedom, "A government which rests upon the opinion of a fully informed people is a democratic government; a government which rests upon the uninformed opinion of citizens from whom information has been withheld by the government itself is a caricature of democratic government." Unfortunately, some of the public officials who take least kindly to cartoons about their policies, themselves engage in just this kind of caricaturing.

In recent years there has been quite a decline in the number of press conferences held by the President and many Cabinet members. And despite habitual references to "weekly press conferences" there have been long

2/22/56   1/22/58

periods when these news sessions were skipped so regularly that the mere fact of a meeting with the press was quite a piece of news in itself.

Even when high officials have met the press, the conferences have sometimes been reminiscent of the old you-don't-say routine. In that comedy bit, a man answers the phone, cries repeatedly, "You don't say! You don't say!" and finally hangs up. When the straight man asks breathlessly, "What did he say?" the answer comes: "He didn't say."

As a part of "the right to know," I think we have a right to expect our officials to know—at least about things that should be of concern to them. In every public poll there is always a group of people listed in a category titled "Don't Know." But I don't think any section of the public should settle for Don't Know government. Nevertheless, inquiries from Washington correspondents have frequently drawn complete blanks from high officials, even when those inquiries have concerned items with which even casual newspaper readers were familiar.

One government action which roused many newspapers to protest was the State Department ban on travel of newsmen to China. It was apparently

"However, We've Been Pretty Successful In Keeping American Newspapermen Out Of China"

1/6/57

"Look—I'll Let A Few Of You Have Dates With Her"

7/21/57

"Children! Think Of The Example You're Setting For Your Elders"

8/15/57

"We're Still Wrestling With It"

3/6/57

"How Dare You Treat Americans The Way We Do?"

5/14/57

the notion of the Secretary of State that we would all be safer if we not only withheld recognition from China but made that land mass of about 3,000,000 square miles terra incognita for Americans. Perhaps he felt that if we didn't notice China at all, it might go away.

Latest reports filtering in from foreign newsmen indicate, however, that there is indeed a place called China; that it has a population of more than 600,000,000 people; that it is a considerable force in Asia; and that it might even be to our advantage to get some firsthand information on what's happening there.

After considerable criticism by newspapers, Secretary Dulles finally allowed that he might permit a limited number of newsmen to travel, because he now found it "desirable" that additional information on China be made available to the American people. And some papers seemed pathetically grateful for this small favor, which was no favor at all. In a sharply critical column, Walter Lippmann wrote:

> . . . by what right, and on what principle, does he claim to have the power to decide how much information it is "desirable" for the American people to have? We have here the unprecedented and impertinent assertion that the right to turn off and the right to turn on the tap of news is one of the prerogatives of the Secretary of State . . .

Mr. Lippmann went on to point out that the power to determine whether, when, where and under what conditions the American press may report news in foreign countries is a usurpation of power, and he concluded by saying that "Mr. Dulles has an imperfect grasp of the principles of a free press in a free society."

Mr. Lippmann's comments seemed to me to be exactly right. But I think also that the issue involved much more than the flow of news through regular channels.

The freedom of the press does not belong exclusively to professional journalists. Except in wartime, I don't know why any American citizen should not be free to come and go as he pleases—at his own risk, in some areas—even if he is only contemplating running off a leaflet on a hand press, or if he has no intention ever to publish at all. He not only has the right to see the world through the eyes of news correspondents; he has the right to know by going and seeing for himself.

I think the professional press would really have been in a stronger position if it had protested earlier and more vigorously about violations of the rights of all Americans. For years the State Department had arbitrarily denied passports to some citizens, even for travel to friendly nations. In one classic case it withheld a passport from a famous American scientist, who later was awarded the Nobel Prize. At that point the government officials (who later conceded their expediency in the matter) reversed their decision and permitted the scientist to go abroad. It was this case which gave rise to the slogan, "Get a Nobel Prize and win a passport."

The whole problem of secrecy which has been of increasing concern to newsmen might very well be traced back to the early "security" procedures of a decade ago. If a government employee could be tossed out of work without even the right to know his accuser, the same thing could be done—and was done—to employees of private companies. And if the right to know could be denied in such a vital area, it could be—and was—denied in many other areas. Everything followed—to use an old phrase particularly appropriate in this case—as night follows day. When the newspapers themselves finally found that a cloak had been tossed over their heads they had a right and a duty to scream. But they shouldn't have been surprised.

There has been a tendency for government to inquire more and more into the lives and thoughts of private citizens, while at the same time denying the right of the people to inquire into their government. These are the two sides of a coin labeled "security," which an increasing number of people

"There Also Seems To Be Some Unrest Among The Americans"

"We're Faced With A Security Crisis. Information Is Still Leaking Into This Country"

4/11/58

5/8/58

"But I Was So Careful To Keep It Safe"

"Maybe This Isn't The Best Way
To Get Security"

11/25/57

4/27/56

have come to recognize as counterfeit. Many public officials (who used to be regarded as public servants) have taken the position, "We'll ask all the questions."

In speaking of excessive secrecy in government, Samuel J. Archibald, staff director of the House Government Information Subcommittee, said, "The most dangerous block to a free flow of information is an attitude—the attitude of the federal official, who, in effect, tells the press and public, 'It's none of your damn business.'"

Others have pointed out the tendency of some men in government to feel that the people are so fragile or so unstable that if they were given the harsh truth about events in the world they couldn't take it. One thing for sure is that we can't take it if we don't get it. My opinion is that we can take anything except government that separates itself from us and withholds the truth from us.

Knowledge is, as the old quotation goes, power. And if political leaders keep from us the knowledge we need, they can not make up for this lack, even by recommending us to a Supreme Power—as many of them do frequently.

Undoubtedly many officials feel that they can decide better than we can

23

"You Act Like You Thought This Was Your Government"

HERBLOCK
©1955 THE WASHINGTON POST CO.

11/13/55

what's best for us. And undoubtedly most officials who interlard their speeches with religious appeals are also sincere in their expressions of divine faith. But in a democratic government, both the people and their officials need to do a good deal more than look heavenward. I think this is pretty well recognized—if not often mentioned out loud—because even the most publicly devout politicians do not suggest that we should rely on Providence to the extent of scrapping our defenses.

I have an uneasy feeling that much of the spiritual faith expressed by politicians—however fine and sincere it may be—is, in a way, offered as a substitute for another faith that many of them have neglected. That is, faith in the people.

It was upon this faith that our government was founded—a faith that involves trust in each other, dedication to free inquiry, and confidence in the collective wisdom of an informed public.

Some of our officials have been so pious in their speeches that they have apparently come to feel that they are constantly in church. Perhaps that explains why they whisper low and keep shushing us. They need to be reminded that they are not in church; they are in public office. Their business is not to tell us what to believe but to protect us in our right to believe or disbelieve as we choose, and to learn as much as we can.

It's probably no coincidence that some of the politicians who are shortest on giving out public information are longest on proclaiming their religious faith and decrying what they keep referring to as "atheistic communism." The essential difference between our nation and all nations under dictatorships, including the Communist ones, is not that ours is a religious country but that it is a free one. But I think there's a good reason why some officials choose to forget that. If they think in terms of freedom there are bound to be disquieting thoughts about some of their policies which ape our adversaries. It's much easier if they can say, "Yeah, but we've got religion." Then they can roll over and go back to sleep—or tell the rest of us to pipe down and go back to sleep.

That attitude has apparently seeped down from high levels to a number of other people. On a pleasant autumn evening in 1957 I was half listening to the radio when my ears shot up as I heard some school children being interviewed about our liberties. They were asked about things like the right of people to speak their opinions freely; and they regarded such ideas as rather dangerous.

The interviewer explained to them that freedom of speech and of the press are included in the Bill of Rights, gave them a brief fill-in on this, and asked what did they think now? The students did not think very much of those rights. And why not? Well, they felt that these things didn't sound very *spiritual.*

Man Overboard

6/17/58

I don't know which chicken or which egg comes first—the right to know or a knowledge of our rights. But they are so closely associated that the answers of the students left me unhappy on both counts.

The impression has somehow been getting around that the right to know is too good for the common people; that human freedom and human welfare are not good enough objectives for government; and that a Miss Liberty who is not bowed in an attitude of prayer is—*pst pst pst*—Not All That She Ought To Be. And that's where I start getting sore.

I like that girl. I like her just the way she is. I don't want to see her scrunched down, doubled up, or shoved into a back room by pious politicians who prefer to keep things dark. We need to have her keep holding that torch as high as she can so we can see just what's going on around here.

"We'd Let You See It But We're Afraid You Might Be Overcome With Joy"

1/3/58

"Secrecy? What Secrecy?"

4/20/58

"Ball? I Haven't Got Your Ball, Kid"

HERBLOCK
©1956 THE WASHINGTON POST CO.

6/4/56

"That's Odd—They Get Answers This Way On TV"

HERBLOCK
©1957 THE WASHINGTON POST CO.

12/27/57

"What Is This—A Game?"

11/4/55

"I Hear You're Still Trying To Eliminate Fallout"

4/14/58

"I Might Do A Little Experimenting With You, Too"

6/19/56

"Rock-A-Bye Baby, In The Tree Top— Let's Make Believe The Fallout Will Stop"

3/22/57

"Notice How Fluffier-Than-Ever White They Are?"

HERBLOCK
©1957 THE WASHINGTON POST Co.

7/15/57

"There—Now You're Pretty"

9/9/56

"Yaaa—You've Been Poisoning The Air, Too. So There!"

9/3/56

"Don't Worry, I Don't Think There's Anything in There"

5/13/57

"Lewis Strauss Says That To Stop Nuclear Tests Would Be A Tragic Mistake"

4/21/58

"Everything's Under Control. I've Got Him On A Leash"

HERBLOCK
©1956 THE WASHINGTON POST CO.

7/22/56

33

"Want To Know How It Ends?"

12/31/56

"They Don't Say *Positively*"

8/12/58

2

"PEOPLE'S REPUBLIC"

"I Said, 'YOU TOO CAN SHARE THE BETTER LIFE!'"

"I Said, 'Say Hello To The Gentleman'—"

7/1/56

10/10/56

"No, No, Men—Just The One On The End"

10/25/56

Handwriting On The Wall

10/29/56

"Ah, You've Come Back To Me"

11/13/56

"Who Else Do We Pick Up In This Car Pool?"

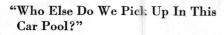

11/27/56

"I'll Be Glad To Restore Peace To The Middle East, Too"

11/6/56

"This Is Strictly An Internal Matter Among Us Doves"

11/22/56

"We'd Love To Have You Drop In Some Other Time"

HERBLOCK
©1956 THE WASHINGTON POST CO

12/5/56

"How Do You Let Go When You've Got Hold Of A Man?"

12/21/56

"There Must Be Some Way We Can Forward March To The Rear"

1/2/57

"How Do We Put Down This Uprising?"

7/2/57

"—This 13th Anniversary Of Your Liberation—"

4/4/58

"Why Don't You Help Me Get This Poor Fellow Back On His Feet?"

1/14/57

"Did I Hear Somebody Knock A Few Months Ago?"

5/6/57

3

PERSONALIZED MENTION

THE PERIODICALS are breaking out all over with articles and photo layouts on a few Presidential aspirants—complete with full sets of pearly teeth, with wives, children and pets, and all oozing personality in every picture and paragraph. With the approach of another big campaign, I can already feel the Madison Avenue squads closing in like clothing-store salesmen, asking, "Now, do you want the gray flannel suit with the two-button jacket or three buttons?" I don't want a gray flannel suit at all. And I can do with a lot less of that personality merchandising.

Personal items have always played a part in politics. Even in the days of Lincoln and Douglas there were undoubtedly voters who were less impressed by the arguments than they were by the fact that a candidate seemed like a nice, homely, down-to-earth feller or that he looked impressive. And in any political situation, the heart or the pocketbook may have reasons and prejudices that the head knows only how to rationalize. But in recent years the personality-peddling has been more highly organized and has been putting issues and debate further into the background.

If this kind of thing goes much further, we may end up taking tape measurements of the candidates' smiles, and having the wives and kiddies stroll down a convention-hall runway, to be judged on points. The candidates themselves can be scored on such activities as their culinary abilities. And, for a grand finale, all the candidates can be put through the equivalent of an old tribal torture ritual, to demonstrate their resiliency and physical hardihood. None of these things would have anything to do with issues, convictions or moral courage. But they would provide comparative tests for the standards by which candidates are often sold—and elected.

All this political personality pushing reminds me of a development I've noticed in advertising. Some time ago, advertisers discovered that millions of avid comic-strip readers would give their attention to comic-strip-type ads, in which the product was mentioned in dialogue "balloons." After a while they found that they could get attention simply by using a photograph of a couple of people talking, with type-set balloons emanating from their mouths. Then they used just a picture of a head speaking the message, with the tail of the balloon pointing in the general direction of the head. And finally they just printed the sales pitch in a balloon emanating from nowhere and with no character visible at all. The political equivalent has been the inflation of "personality" balloons to a point where they tend to shove out of the picture continuity, action and character. And these projections have become so synthetic that they've even distorted personality itself.

With a popular and personable hero like General Eisenhower, the merchandisers had a good public-relations product to start with, and they made the most of it. Abetted—let's face it—by much of the press, they expanded an attractive personality into a kind of national good-luck symbol that was not only above the battle but practically above the Presidency. And there was developed a we-love-you-just-because-you're-you attitude that would brook no debate.

Odd as it may seem, the cartoons that I do—even with all the faces and physical exaggerations in them—are not essentially personal. And I don't really care how charming or forbidding characters may be as individuals. Where public figures are shown, they are nearly always related to some current situation—some issue that they're dealing with, or that I think they *should* be dealing with. But from 1952 to 1957, some people found even in traditional caricatures an almost shocking irreverence.

In the spring of 1956 I did the "How Do You Do?" cartoon, on the developing Middle East crisis, which is shown on the opposite page. It brought me a letter from a lady who was both hurt and indignant. She wrote that she was on to my little game and that the figure in that drawing, labeled "Administration," was nothing more nor less than "a thinly veiled picture of our President."

I was sorry to read that letter, which made me feel that I must have fallen down in the drawing if anyone could think that the likeness was meant to be veiled even in the thinnest way. But I was sorrier still that there were those who felt that a President had nothing to do with government policies, or that political criticism must be surreptitious. Shades of Thomas Nast and Finley Peter Dunne and a long line of others, I thought. What were we coming to if any public figures were held to be above caricature and comment?

The question was purely rhetorical because I had a pretty good idea what we were coming to—and had, in fact, arrived at. We were in a strange state

44

"How Do You Do"

3/7/56

45

where politics had become as impersonally "personalized" as a press-agent piece in a movie fan magazine; and where admiration had, in many cases, curdled into adulation.

The eulogizing of Glorious Leaders is something that cartoonists and writers on the other side of the Iron Curtain can do better—and better do. But in our country, the principle function of the press is to keep a not-too-starry eye on government. It's easy to criticize, as people always say; and for quite a while there I wondered why more weren't doing it.

Because I'm interested in politics—and criticism—the Eisenhower Administration and the newer developments in political public relations fascinated me as political phenomena.

I don't recall the elections of Grant or McKinley, despite anything the newer copy boys may say. But I do have some recollections of peace-and-prosperity in the twenties; and of another President who was not noted for vigor in the executive office but was a comfortable old shoo-in for election. Coolidge was popular but the object of some pretty sharp satire. He may have been regarded as the Keeper Of The Golden Calf, but he was not the idol itself. And his custodianship did not pass for great leadership.

Taking a quick backward look at the peak popularity years of the Eisenhower Administration, I think the feeling about Ike was different. And to make up the difference you'd have had to throw in, along with Coolidge, Peace and Prosperity, somebody like Rudolph Valentino—and a five-star hat.

Of course, there is always a keen public interest in any President. Whatever he says makes news. If he's taciturn, that's noted too. In the absence of solid statements and strong action a corps of correspondents will translate the lines in his face into lines of copy. And there are then more personal pieces and more statements by press secretaries. Significantly, there was probably never an Administration in which Presidential press secretaries and press agents played so important a role as they did under Mr. Eisenhower.

During both terms some of the biggest headlines were made by the President's physical condition. The stock ticker echoed the Presidential pulse. And during his illnesses and convalescences there were flashed across the country reports and diagrams of a kind never before equaled in intimacy outside of commercials for home remedies.

All this was of interest to millions of people and was, for the most part, legitimate news. I too was concerned about the President's physical condition, even if I didn't follow all the details of a tooth extraction. But I was also concerned about the condition of the national political health. Consideration of possible Presidential disability was okay. But what about consideration of plain Presidential ability?

Everything had become so personalized that the state of the President and the state of the nation were widely considered to be one and the same thing.

"What's Your Prognosis For November, Doctor?"

"I Feel Fine, Doc. I Just Want An Analysis Of The Political Situation"

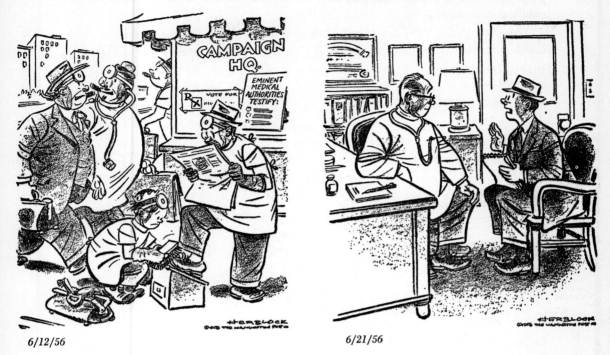

6/12/56

6/21/56

By 1956 it was not a question whether Mr. Eisenhower should run for re-election; it was just a question whether he *would* run.

By a lot of people he seemed to be regarded as a sort of wonder of nature. It was enough simply that he should be there. And to some extent, Mr. Eisenhower himself may have been taken in by his own political press agents and campaign orators. They had long hammered away on the themes of Korea, Communism and Corruption. And perhaps he really got to believing that his predecessors were such villains that it was a pretty good deal for the country to have in the White House a man who was simply a peace-loving, patriotic sort of fellow. If that was the case, I think he seriously under-estimated both the job and the men he followed in it.

Many of my drawings of President Eisenhower—when he reported himself as feeling fit and on duty—have shown him in various attitudes of inactivity when problems cried out for attention. It seemed to me that the President, who had often expressed his belief in the principle of separation of powers, too often separated himself from his own powers. But for about five years every-thing seemed perfectly satisfactory to a lot of people who had previously placed personal blame on a President for anything unfortunate that hap-

"Ever Think Of Starting The Motor?"   **"Congress Just Isn't Giving Us Much Leadership"**

7/16/56   8/22/57

pened during his Administration, including the spread of crab grass on their lawns.

To many of them, the duties of the Presidency underwent a remarkable change in January 1953. Some even seemed to have changed their concept of the job of government itself—to one in which its duty was to secure domestic tranquilizers, provide a pretty common type of defense, and promote the general's welfare.

There were times when a guy who believed in normal criticism and discussion almost got to feeling like the lonesome man in a city far from home who walked up to a stranger and said, "Mister, do you believe in God? I'll take either side."

I won't take "either side" in discussions, but I do like plain talk and honest argument. And there was such a dearth of this, particularly in the Administration, that I even developed a strange, warm feeling—which had nothing to do with policies—for Secretary of Defense Charles Wilson. His statements, whether about bird dogs or dunghills, not only were colorful but represented a definite viewpoint. And in discussing armament expenditures, he even

"Leave Something For Me, Charlie"

9/19/57

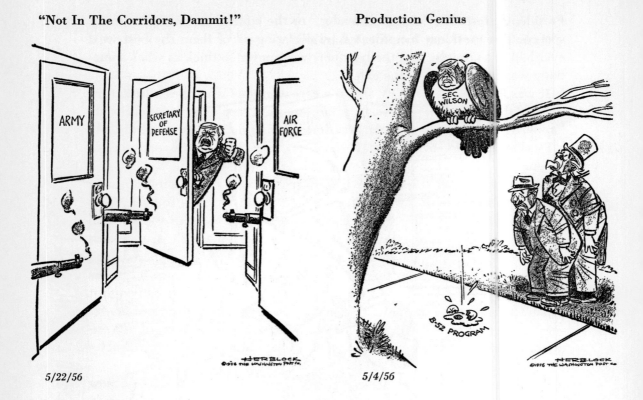

5/22/56   5/4/56

pointed out that part of the increased costs was due to inflation, which was at that time considered by most of his colleagues to be a dirty word.

He had the virtue of saying what he thought, even if what he thought didn't strike some of us as being very good. And in that respect his comments were better than most of the vague statements we got in Washington. Those were pretty confusing, although generally things didn't get *really* confusing until the issuance of clarifying statements.

What came through mostly was the colossal press-agentry about how dandy things were under peachy personalities. And this remained pretty effective until the late-1957 combination of sputniks going up, an economic chart going down, and a two-term President already on the way out.

I don't think it would be fair to say that Mr. Eisenhower shrank in the office. I think he stayed about the same size all the time. It was the big built-up merchandised mythology that shrank and cracked away—the super-duper product that was NOW finer, better, more patriotic, more human, more nonpartisan, more peace-loving, more honest, more good-natured, more gentlemanly, more *genuinely sincere*, heroic, vitamin-enriched and bigger, yes, folks, bigger BIGGER BIGGER than anything you've ever seen in politics before.

Everybody was bigger and better. Most of the high officials around the

50

President referred to "our great leader," or the equivalent, in almost every speech. The President reciprocated by declaring all of them the best we'd ever had in *their* jobs; and the bouquets were never so thick as when somebody was being eased to the exit.

It was like one of those TV shows where everyone who does a little turn is one of the truly *great* performers of our time, and each of them is deliriously happy to be on this wonderful wonderful program. It wasn't merely *like* a TV show; it frequently *was* a TV show—and for a long time a very successful one.

At the end of 1957 the purveyors of "personality" didn't slow down in their work; they switched to another product. Mr. Eisenhower found himself suddenly downgraded by erstwhile supporters who, up until the election of 1956, had impressed upon him and the country the idea that he was practically indispensable. Even *Time* magazine, which had labored long to protect its readers from doubts about the President, let them in on the news that his prestige was slipping and called for more action—although it explained that the confusion in Washington was a "healthy kind of confusion." Nothing could better have demonstrated the predicament of a President unable to run for another term, unless it would have been disavowal by the National Committee itself.

There was then unveiled the New Nixon, who was promoted like a new Miss Rheingold. He was now, *now, NOW* new *new NEW*—more vibrant, more power-packed, more chock full of vim and personality, with filter-tip speeches and finger-tip steering.

I have never been impressed about the talk of a "new Nixon." It always seemed to me like talking about a new chameleon every time one of those creatures took on a different color. The chief characteristic of a chameleon is that it *does* change color. And Mr. Nixon's career has shown him to be consistently a man of varying hues and stripes—not to mention checkers.

In the cartoons I have sometimes pictured him not as a chameleon but as a political cat—basking in the sun, watching which way to jump, and wondering what's in it for him. These drawings brought me several letters of complaint from cat lovers; and I had to explain to them that I have a cat of my own—nothing personal.

The 1958 model didn't seem to me to be essentially different from all the previous new Nixons. I think he "grew" to the extent that people grew tired of his smear campaigns against men like Senators Carroll, O'Mahoney and Neuberger—and grew tired of cracks like "Isn't it wonderful finally to have a Secretary of State who is not taken in by the Communists?"

But the Nixon who, in June 1958, saw nothing politically improper in the Sherman Adams–Bernard Goldfine relationship (and who assured fellow party members that "the public memory is short") was exactly the same Nixon with exactly the same moral standards as the one who had, in 1952, "ex-

Sunshine

11/6/57

"Well, Men, What'll We Refrain From Doing Now?"

4/28/58

"Now You Kids Beat It"

10/26/56

"Dick, If I Could Borrow Checkers— Hello? Hello?—"

5/7/56

plained" his own acceptance of $18,235 from a group of Californians with special legislative interests.

I know that some correspondents have been grateful to the Vice-President for giving them "personal" inside-dope stories—which, by a curious coincidence, also provided him with favorable publicity. And I know that some have been impressed by the efficiency of a candidate who, so to speak, made the campaign trains run on time. But even in these days of mechanization, synthetics, and panzer press-agentry, I guess I'm not yet ready for Artificial Man—at least not in the White House.

One unhappy effect of high-power political personality plugging has been to create a confusion between personal success and national success. And on occasions, the mere continued existence and functioning of a "personality" has been regarded not only as a cause for congratulation but as a national triumph.

It was at the time of the French Revolution (the old *old* French Revolution, that is) that Abbé Sieyès said, when asked what he had done during the Reign of Terror, "I have survived." The politics of personality has, in turn, given us what might be called the politics of survival.

When President Eisenhower survived his illnesses and even pressed on to attend conferences in Latin America and in Paris, we were glad and we admired his fortitude. But unfortunately, that did not mean that the conferences themselves were successful.

The Nixon Presidential candidacy was itself the product of the politics of survival. He became a leading contender for the nomination, not because his career particularly commended him for the high position, but because cold actuarial logic indicated that he might survive his chief. And party members flocked to his band wagon because, in the event of Presidential disability, he was the boy most likely to succeed to office before the 1960 convention.

When the Vice-President returned from his ill-fated, or ill-advised, Latin American tour in 1958, he was given—with some planning by his party's political organization—an ovation. Again, we were all glad that an official, and his wife, had escaped serious misfortune. And we were, additionally, united in deploring indignities by a few hoodlums upon one who represented our government. But that did not make the tour an American success. It was, in fact, a disaster. However, few people asked, "Was this trip necessary?" or "Why wasn't it better planned?" He had survived.

Much as I may disagree with some of them, I wish all political personalities —and their charming families—good health and long life. But I wish also for a healthier and livelier national interest in basic issues, policies and political morality. Personal press-agentry is not enough. Personal survival is not enough. And national survival is not enough, either. A country of 175,000,000 people can do better than that.

"Let's See—What'll I Wear Today?"

2/15/56

54

"You Said It, Pal—We Both Got A Right To Poison The Air"

10/5/56

"Oh, Brother!"

10/4/56

"Yeah, I Mentioned Your Name"

8/29/57

"Thanks A Lot, Fellows"

11/7/57

**"We Wait Till He Begins To Act Restless,
See? Then We Sort Of Mosey Up
To Him—"**

Medical Consultation

11/17/55

12/14/55

"Shall We Walk A Little Faster?"

"Yahoooo!"

1/30/56

3/1/56

*On President Eisenhower's announcement that he
would run for re-election*

"You Came Here Your Very Self!"

REPUBLICAN
NATIONAL
CONVENTION
1956

HERBLOCK
©1956 THE WASHINGTON POST CO.

8/22/56

"Sorry—Wrong Number"

7/26/56

"Act Dignified—Look Alert—And Remember, We're All Very, Very Proud of Richard Nixon"

8/20/56

"Well, Men, That Buttons It Up"

8/23/56

"Harold Has Been Rehabilitated"

8/24/56

"Look—A Joke Is A Joke—"

8/29/56

"Boy, Have They Got A Personality Cult Over Here!"

10/28/56

"Gosh, What A Frightening Creature!"

10/18/56

Boom!

10/30/56

With The Greatest Of Ease

HERBLOCK
©1956 THE WASHINGTON POST CO.

11/8/56

"Go Away, Boy—You Bother Me"

HERBLOCK
©1956 THE WASHINGTON POST CO.

11/5/56

"I Wasn't Beaten In Any Election"

HERBLOCK
©1956 THE WASHINGTON POST CO

11/23/56

"Think There's Been Enough Meeting Of Minds Yet?"

HERBLOCK
©1958 THE WASHINGTON POST CO.

1/17/58

"Great System"

HERBLOCK
©1958 THE WASHINGTON POST CO

5/22/58

"How Did You Say Their Election Came Out?"

HERBLOCK
©1957 THE WASHINGTON POST CO.

11/20/57

On Governor Stevenson's service as consultant to the State Department

"Ezra, I Don't Know What We'd Do Without You"

9/18/57

12/11/55

"Not Yet"

2/25/58

"And Some Day We May Improve Delivery Service"

2/29/56

"What Do You Suppose He Means This Time?"

HERBLOCK
©1957 THE WASHINGTON POST CO.

7/25/57

64

The Helicopter Era

HERBLOCH
© 1957 THE WASHINGTON POST CO

3/27/57

4

CHRONOLOGICAL DISORDER

AT A TIME when physical science has an impact on everything including political science, I don't want to be left behind; and I've been trying to dredge up some odds and ends from an old high-school course that might be useful these days. I have a small stock of phrases like "warm air rises" and "water seeks its level," which will probably come in handy somewhere, especially if they are delivered with a knowing nod of the head. But so far I haven't been able to work them into any discussions of nuclear physics or outer space, or even of plain old-fashioned politics.

I have one, though, that fits in almost anywhere: *Nature abhors a vacuum.* It's true. It's universal. World powers abhor a vacuum. Politicians abhor a vacuum. Disorder and violence rush into vacuums. And nowhere has this been better illustrated than in the integration problem.

The Supreme Court handed down its momentous decision on May 17, 1954, and implemented that decision on May 31, 1955.

In that period, and for some time afterward, there were a few scattered demonstrations but none of great significance. In fact, the immediate reaction of some politicians who later defied the rulings was to accept the inevitability of the change.

But there was an almost ear-shattering silence from the executive branch of government on this issue. There was a complete absence of the kind of moral leadership which, through firm but friendly statements, conferences, and commissions, might have employed the enormous prestige of the Presidency to smooth the way for integration. And the vacuum was hardly filled by vague phrases—in reply to questions—which expressed the views that we all had our opinions, that you can't change the hearts of men by laws, and (when pushed to the limit) that the Court's rulings were, after all, the law of the land.

Against this vacuum pressure began mounting; White Citizens councils were organized, and advocates of disorder were provided with a "respectable" front by the "massive resistance" program of the Byrd machine in Virginia. But on the other side of the Potomac all was quiet; and Senator Byrd, as a budget-watcher, even received kind words from the White House.

The Supreme Court decision itself had been moderate. It had taken into account the mores of communities and had not required that change proceed in all areas at a uniform pace. But there was allowed to grow throughout much of the South the impression that "moderation" consisted of something between the "extremes" of the rock throwers, on the one hand, and the U.S. Supreme Court, on the other. And the real Southern moderates found themselves more and more squeezed out and silenced.

Action reached a climax at Little Rock, when Governor Faubus called out the guard to "preserve law and order" by preventing the carrying out of court orders and local plans, and when the President later sent federal troops to the area. By this time the situation had literally "disintegrated" to a point where nothing else could be done except to send U.S. troops. But as some observers noted at the time, the White House statement did not give the right reason for the action. Federal intervention was needed not simply because of mob violence, but because the Governor of Arkansas himself had forcibly defied the law by using troops to keep the Negro children *out* of school.

In this case, as in others where violence had broken out, nothing much came of the dispatch of FBI men to the scene (a little late) or of threats of federal prosecution. And there seemed to be no follow-up either on the Administration's pre-Little Rock talk of demands for a "stronger" civil-rights bill than Congress approved.

At a White House press conference held August 27, 1958—on the eve of an extraordinary session of the Supreme Court to consider the Little Rock case—President Eisenhower finally gave some idea of his feelings on the school integration question. He indicated a preference for a "slower" approach. This remarkable expression of opinion came four years and three months after the original Court ruling.

The cartoons follow in general chronological—and logical—sequence. They do not include all the violent incidents or all the sidelights. One odd item, however, might be mentioned as a footnote to the Little Rock story. In January 1958, a national vice-commander and a former national commander of the American Legion participated with the Arkansas Department of that organization in presenting to Governor Orval Faubus the state group's "Americanism" award.

"Carry Me Back To Old Virginny"

11/16/55

"Tote Dat Barge! Lift Dat Boycott! Ride Dat Bus!"

3/25/56

2/13/56

Bus Stop

4/24/55

"Somebody From Outside Must Have Influenced Them"

2/28/56

"Tsk Tsk—Somebody Should Do Something About That"

HERBLOCK
©1956 THE WASHINGTON POST CO.

4/3/56

"Help! Man-Eating Tiger!"

7/18/56

"The Mean Old Federal Courts Are Trying To Impose Their Will On Others"

9/20/56

"I Said There'd Be Trouble, And I Won't Have You Making A Liar Out Of Me"

9/23/56

"We Forget How It Got There, But It's Sacred"

1/3/57

"After All, It's Only Been A Couple Of Years Since The Supreme Court Decision"

9/5/56

72

"We Must Protect Minority Rights—For Senators, That Is"

1/4/57

"Just A Little More Watering Down"

7/19/57

"I'd Rather See You Dead Than Compromised"

8/7/57

"Miss What's-Your-Name, I've Fallen In Love With You"

8/24/57

The Gov. Faubus "Peace" Plan

9/5/57

"I Think We've Managed To Save His Face"

9/17/57

"Oh, Say, Can You See?"

9/24/57

Back To School

9/25/57

"This Is An Explosive Situation"

HERBLOCK
©1957 THE WASHINGTON POST CO.

9/6/57

Tears

9/10/57

"Oh, Boy—Lots Of Headlines"

9/13/57

"How Can You Doubt My Good Intentions?"

10/3/57

"Who Said Anything About Local Rights?"

11/1/57

"It's Getting So You Can Hardly Stone People In Peace Any More"

10/1/57

"Later On, I'd Like To Ask You Something"

9/30/57

8/20/58

"And All This Time I Was Hoping You'd Speak Up"

HERBLOCK
©1958 THE WASHINGTON POST CO.

8/28/58

80

5

THE TIME OF THE
SPUTNIKS

It seems like only a few years ago that we were entering into the bright new Air Age. Then, all of a sudden, we were in the Atomic Age—which soon became the Nuclear Age. And here we are already in the Space Age. The effect of all this has been to make a lot of us conscious of just plain Age. And the stories about what we might expect in the future don't make us feel any younger or sprightlier either.

The feature writers keep telling us that new horizons are opening up which will make the first airplane flights and the first ocean crossings seem as nothing by comparison. A trip to the moon is reported to be only a few years off; and already hundreds of people are said to have volunteered to crouch in capsules for journeys out of this world.

Well, if I'm not there with my pneumatic suit and Space Diary when the count-downs begin, they can just go ahead without me. With every passing year I feel less and less urge to blast off anywhere except to my own little bed. I guess I'm going to be just an old stick-in-the-earth, poking along on one planet while the younger fellows zoom on to greener or brighter spheres.

In time they'll be coming back from their space voyages to tell us of exciting places they've discovered, and comparing notes on quaint craters where they've stopped. That's when I'm going to light my good old pipe, take a few puffs on it, find that it's gone out, and throw it back in the drawer with all the other good old pipes I've never learned to like.

"I've seen some pretty interesting things in my time, too," I'll say. Then, a little louder to cover their groans: "Take off your space helmets and gather round." And while the young bloods slump down in their chairs, I'll tell them How Science And Learning Came Back To Washington In The Late Nineteen-Fifties.

The first real news I heard about space objects was on July 30, 1955. I was leaning on the city-room water cooler thinking about nothing farther away than the coffee shop across the street, when somebody showed me a bulletin that had just ticked in, alerting papers that an important announcement was coming from the White House. As the afternoon passed, more tantalizing bulletins rattled off the machines, advising that the announcement would have to do with outer space. This was pretty exciting stuff, and soon a crowd of us were gathered around the tickers.

Finally the announcement came that the United States planned to launch an earth satellite during the 1957–1958 geophysical year, and that it would be about the size of a basketball. One of the newsmen felt this was a little anticlimatic and murmured, "Gee, from the advance buildup, I thought they were gonna tell us they already had a satellite running on schedule, with a hostess aboard."

That probably doesn't sound very funny to you fellows who travel in super space vehicles, but back in those days when we flew only in airplanes that was kind of an amusing thought.

The prospect of even a small satellite was a big story, just the same, and was soon the talk of the whole proud country. Twenty-six months later, the first man-made moon was actually shot into space, and the news was sensational. The only thing that marred our pleasure in this historic achievement was that it had been launched not by us, but by the Russians. Our government had been the first to get the mimeograph machines orbiting; but there wasn't much comfort in that. In fact, with U.S. prestige hitting a new low, some people were even irritated by it. And matters were not improved any when the Russians sent up another and bigger satellite containing a little dog who seemed to be laughing to see such sportnik.

There we were moonwatching those things; and, as you might say, now we saw through a glass darkly or through the dark glassily. Actually, people took all this pretty much in stride; but it made them think some, and that's where the real excitement began to come in.

Every once in a while somebody would scratch his head and ask, "Gosh, how did this happen?" And then our political leaders would cry, "Don't get panicky! *Don't get panicky!*" Some of them would get to carrying on about how it was all the fault of the people who had been running the government five years before; and it was enough to wrench your heart when some of them got to wandering and moaning about Pearl Harbor and the boys in Korea and things like that. Then we'd have to quiet them down and put cold cloths on their heads and hold their hands till they stopped trembling. And all the time they'd be shouting at us to be calm! Be calm! *Be calm!* Those were pretty trying times, I can tell you.

You young fellows with your interplanetary studies probably can't imagine

HERBLOCK
©1957 THE WASHINGTON POST CO.

10/8/57

"Wonder Why We're Not Keeping Pace?"

a time when the government didn't pay much attention to science and thought basic research was a waste of time; but that's the way it was in that particular period. And after those sputniks went up, when we read in the papers that a scientist had been invited to a White House dinner, that had us leaping out of our chairs. True, this fellow was a rocket expert—what you might call more of a military scientist. But there he was among a lot of people sitting down to dinner with the Head Man, just as if he was an important corporation executive or a big campaign contributor or something. There was no use anyone telling us that nothing had changed when we read *that*.

A lot of things had changed; but in a way you might say everything was the same. What I mean is that most of the people who made the statements you read in the papers sounded just about the way each of them had before.

Some of them had been telling us for years that we needed more science and education and research, and that even our defenses were going to suffer if we didn't do something about those things. I used to draw pictures about what they said. Take this one here about the race, for example—that was done seven months or so before the first sputnik. And if I just showed you kids the dates you might be impressed and think that things like this were based on inside stuff. But they weren't, unless you'd include in that category stuff on the inside pages of the papers. All of it was right there for anybody who wanted to read it—even our leaders, if they'd been interested in reading.

Well, a few Congressional committee fellows who attributed everything to spies—they ran true to form too. Some of them had always figured that whenever any other country developed something, it must have stolen the secrets from us. These fellows were so busting with patriotism that they considered the idea of anybody outside the U.S. doing any thinking to be unthinkable. So they stuck with their theories too and claimed that the sputnik plans were all stolen from us. If the spies did that, I guess they must have stolen all the carbon copies and everything, because we spent quite a while just trying to catch up with the big satellite-launching engines they had over there.

And I remember hearing one radio news reader who used to toss in bold, brave editorializations whenever he got to any items about Russia. When he read us the news about that sputnik he told us how sneaky the Russians had been in sending it up without first telling us just when they were going to do it. What really turned out to be kind of tricky, even if the Russians didn't plan it that way, was the way they used to claim having invented everything from the cotton gin to the wireless. These ex post facto inventions of theirs got to be such a joke that when our scientists tried to tell us about the real progress the Russians were making, people would get to laughing so hard they couldn't hear. Looking back on it, I guess maybe the Russian government had put out all those stories to build up morale and scientific interest over there. But on that satellite stuff they had us laughing out of the other side of our faces, as we used to say.

Our President kept pretty cool, same as always. Well, nearly always, anyhow. He said he wasn't disturbed one iota about the sputnik. He and other officials explained that we hadn't been in a race with the Russians anyhow; and besides, we didn't want to use military devices to launch a scientific thing; and furthermore there was nothing to worry about because the satellite was not a weapon. Apparently it was sort of a gadget.

Some people were a little concerned anyhow, because the sputnik seemed to prove what we'd been hearing about the Russians being able to launch long-range missiles. And a special Presidential assistant on national-security affairs was very unhappy because a magazine called *Aviation Week* reported that our own government had been tracking those Russian missiles for two years. He was even reported, in the New York *Journal of Commerce*, as having told an audience that the article was treasonable. But it was sure interesting to the rest of us who hadn't been told about such developments. Talk about missiles in Russia—we hadn't even been able to break the sound barrier in Washington.

"He's Sure Been Kept Under Wraps, All Right"

"Yoo Hoo, Everybody!"

11/12/57

10/25/57

Official comment on our position vis à vis Russia's ranged from the general pooh-pooh statements, through explanations that nobody could tell just how things stood, to a remark made by Neil McElroy, who had just become Secretary of Defense. Mr. McElroy was new on the team and perhaps he didn't understand how to act. In answer to reporters' questions, he said it was "rather obvious that we are behind the Russians" in the missiles-satellite race. These words from a high official were so straightforward they were practically breath-taking; and a number of people began talking about this new Cabinet member as a possible candidate for President.

I guess the most interesting statements of all came from the Vice-President, who said that the government would have to finance a satellite-and-missile program by making sharp cuts in domestic spending. He made a stirring speech telling Americans to get away from their weeping walls and to get behind our missile people and help them. "We've got work to do," he said. "Let's get on with it like Americans." That certainly sounded affirmative, except that you got the feeling he was talking to the wrong fellows. Unless he had expected us average guys to build satellites in our back yards, there wasn't much we could do to get on with the job. It was really the men running the government who should have been doing that.

Oh, but he was a good talker, though. No, I wouldn't say he made you forget your troubles, exactly. He just sort of made you forget that he and his friends had anything to do with them.

For example, that talk went so well that a little later he made one to the American Football Coaches Association, possibly figuring that they should punt something into space for us. Anyhow, this was an occasion that had just the right All-American atmosphere, and he put in a lot of sports phrases, which showed he was a regular guy. And as you took in his words, you could practically smell the locker room.

"This is no time to get out the crying towel or to throw in the sponge," he said. And it was grand to hear such vigorous statements. Of course, here again, it was a little as if somebody on a fumbling football team had walked over to the stands and reprimanded the audience for not cheering enough. But it sounded fine. And he warned against anybody making a political football out of security. That was particularly impressive because it wasn't coming from some theoretical dreamer or idle observer. We knew we were getting it straight from a fellow who had plenty of experience at making political footballs out of security. It's always nice to get advice like that from a guy who really knows his subject. And he said that "pessimistic talk" about our position in relation to Russian progress was "unmitigated nonsense."

That was *very* encouraging. Only a year or so before the young man had been saying that proposals for agreements to suspend nuclear tests were "catastrophic nonsense." It was good to know that people who were concerned about what was going on in the world were now guilty only of unmitigated nonsense. It showed they must be improving.

Maybe he was referring to the national-security committee which a short time before had prepared for the government the Gaither report. That document said that our country was in the gravest danger in its history and was moving toward the status of a second-class world power. We wouldn't have known what was in that report except that it was disclosed by a newspaperman named Chalmers Roberts—because the government didn't put it out at all. And I guess the Vice-President must have given the fellows on that commission a real talking-to for writing that kind of pessimistic stuff.

Well, he wound up his speech with a defense of American scientists; and it was thrilling. It just made you itch to get at those darned American People who were attacking our scientists. But this feeling wore off after a while. When you stopped to think about it, the American people weren't attacking our scientists at all; they were complaining about an Administration that had not made proper use of our scientists. And when you stopped to think about it a little more, you remembered that top scientists like Condon and Oppenheimer had been driven out of government service by politicians like the Vice-President himself. But it would have been a pity to spoil such grand oratorical performances by analyzing what was said.

The Vice-President was a master at performing the difficult maneuver which might be called Fleeing The Scene Of The Crime Until They Catch Up With You, And Then Standing Up In The Stirrups And Crying, "Forward, Men!" And that's one that takes real skill.

I tell you about all this because some of you cocky young space travelers think you're pretty clever. But I want you to know that when it comes to careful calculation and split-second timing, you scientific boys couldn't hold a candle to some of the politicians we used to have.

Well, even with all the pep talks, we were a little edgy. Or, I should say, we got kind of nervous *because* of all those talks. It seemed that we private citizens were really to blame for our country's troubles. We hadn't been optimistic enough. And we hadn't been making enough sacrifices. That was another thing we kept hearing.

Some of us would gather in little groups and try to figure out what sacrifices we should be making. There would always be some wise guy who would say that he was ready to sacrifice our great leaders; but the times were too serious for remarks like that. The question of what sacrifices to make was a real problem.

I thought some of giving up cigarettes, but I wasn't sure that this would be enough to pull the country through. With some wrenches and blowtorches we could probably strip from our cars the tail fins that lit up like pinball machines. But there was no use doing this till the government issued the call for them and told us where to leave them.

"Those Crazy Egghead Scientists—If You Didn't Hold 'Em Down They'd Want To Reach For The Moon"

10/9/57

It was a situation that was enough to give us all a national guilt complex. It got so that you could hardly sip a cocktail without wondering if you were holding up the defense program, because maybe the alcohol in that drink would be needed as antifreeze for the engine of some unbuilt missile.

Perhaps we should be paying more taxes? But nobody had asked for those either. In fact, we had been told everything was lovely. And with the government keeping to itself so much information on our defenses and Russia's progress, we couldn't even guess very well how much we *should* be spending. All that was clear was that we had somehow failed our leaders.

You can imagine what a relief it was when they finally let us know what sacrifices we needed to make. To meet the challenge of Russian science, technology and education we were going to have to give up the hope of things like a federal school-construction program. Now we could rest easier because we knew what we had been doing wrong. We had been planning to spend too much on essentials like schools.

During the time of the sputniks there was probably nothing that got more of a going-over than education. And it was wonderful to see how many people who never seemed to care much about our schools before were suddenly excited about them.

People who had always been ready to call for the tar and feathers if a teacher so much as hinted that the Russians were good at anything were now loudly demanding to know why our school methods were not patterned after the Russian ones.

There were also hardheaded realists who had long insisted that the schools waste less time on mental gymnastics and give more good practical training that would be useful in everyday jobs. And here they were now, shouting that those darn old schools weren't utilizing full time to pound math and science into the children's noggins. They pointed out that the schools needed to be stricter, too—that there was too much of what was called "progressive education."

Even back in those days I had been out of school for some time, so I couldn't say very well how it was with the schools' curricula. But there was certainly nothing too progressive about the condition of our national school facilities, which had been falling apart for a couple of decades—or about teachers' salaries, which were still further behind the times. Even in higher learning it didn't take any higher mathematics to figure the income of professors. But, of course, there were exceptions; some of them made almost as much as day laborers.

You want to hear some figures on what it was like with the schools? I still have 'em.

At the end of 1957, U.S. Commissioner of Education Lawrence G. Derthick quoted school estimates of a shortage of 135,000 teachers. And the Rocke-

"Let's See—We Could Put Up Some New Post Offices"

4/13/54

"Something Seems To Have Stunted Them"

10/7/55

An Apple For The Teacher

11/25/55

"Poor Little Kid"

7/8/56

"Now Let's See You Bring Him In"

"Ain't She A Beaut?"

7/22/57

5/6/56

feller Brothers Fund report said that there was a shortage of 142,000 classrooms, and that there were 1,943,000 pupils in excess of normal classroom capacity. This report said we were in an educational crisis.

So this is where we were when those first sputniks went up. Three months later, in his 1958 State of the Union message, President Eisenhower told us what he thought needed to be done. I can give you the exact quote. Emphasizing the need for action outside the federal government, he said:

> In both education and research, redoubled exertions will be necessary on the part of all Americans if we are to rise to the demands of our times. This means hard work on the part of state and local governments, private industry, schools and colleges, private organizations and foundations, teachers, parents, and—perhaps most important of all—the student himself, with his bag of books and his homework.

The teachers, colleges and schools were already working pretty hard to make ends meet. And the student was having to work harder all the time

accurate statements" made by the Chamber of Commerce. And on April 4, the President—still right there with his Secretary of Health, Education, and Welfare—said that federal help was needed to help build classrooms because it was "beyond the power of the states to do it."

On July 22, 1957, Secretary Folsom emerged from a White House meeting to tell reporters that he hoped the President would exert pressure on Congressmen to assure passage of the school bill. This was a little surprising, because it's unusual for a Cabinet member to come away from a talk with the President expressing hope that the boss will support something they're both presumably hot for.

On July 23, the day the House agreed to take up the school bill, there was even more surprising news. Following a morning meeting between the President and his Congressional leaders, the White House disclosed that the President would "accept" the school bill if passed but was not very enthusiastic about it. This was the bill which Secretary Folsom had described as one which did not follow the President's recommendations in every detail but which was, on the whole, "a good bill" and "represents the only real opportunity for effective action this year."

A White House press conference had been scheduled for the following day, July 24, and correspondents were eager to ask the President about the school bill. This press conference was canceled.

On July 25, the House voted on school construction. And in a final effort to get passage of a measure on which there would be no grounds for quibbling, Democratic and Republican advocates of school aid tried to offer the President's own bill. They awaited a call from the White House, but the call never came. On a motion to kill the bill then under consideration, school construction was defeated by a vote of 208–203. On a roll-call vote, 111 Republicans and 97 Democrats voted to kill the bill; and 126 Democrats and 77 Republicans voted against the motion. Three votes, which would have spelled the difference between defeat and victory, were cast against the bill by the President's own Congressional leaders.

On July 31, the delayed White House press conference was held, and the recent school bill was still a big topic. In the questioning on this subject one reporter pointed out, "They [the Democrats] were willing to go along with your bill; and their complaint is that you failed to go to bat for the legislation, so to speak."

The President replied, "I never heard that. . . . If that is true, why, you are telling me something I never heard."

"They say had you spoken up for the legislation it would have passed," concluded the reporter.

In defending his role, Mr. Eisenhower said, "I don't get up and make statements every twenty minutes." And he added a little later that he be-

"Nobody Can Say I Wouldn't Do Something For Him"

7/26/57

"You'll Be Glad To Know I Found Your Lost Cat"

HERBLOCK
©1958 THE WASHINGTON POST CO.

5/2/58

lieved "we should take a look at this question of need honestly, and meet it, and meet it today, and I tell you this: I will have another bill ready for the next session of Congress."

Some newspapers dusted off and ran again the old headline, "Ike To Fight For School Bill Next Year." But next year (1958) the President proposed a modest scholarship program and offered no school-construction bill at all.

On May 7, 1958, it was announced that President Eisenhower was reluctantly accepting the resignation of Secretary Folsom, who agreed to stay on till July and who was reported to be ailing.

That's where my research report ended, because by that time I wasn't feeling so good either. I listened to the children outside, coming home from their half-day at school, and put aside my pencil and papers. I was getting real tired, and felt I had looked over all the old records and had read all the fine political statements I could bear for a while.

Well, that's the way things went back in those days. Some said that the sputniks woke us up, but I don't know. After we finally hoisted a couple of grapefruit-size satellites of our own and began hearing talk of shooting the moon before the next election, I think a lot of people went back to slumberland again.

I've been running on here quite a bit; but I thought you kids ought to know something of how it was when the Space Age began, because that's kind of educational too. And I think there's a lesson in it for you.

You young fellows couldn't have got jet-propelled to the moon just on the hot air from politicians; and you're not going to get to Mars that way either. It's all very well to whoosh around through space in souped-up rockets with longer and longer nose cones on them. But you've got to get back to home base enough to keep an eye on what the government is doing.

I mean you can't just leave things back here to people who act as if education and research are necessary nuisances or something—or as if scientists and scholars are guys to be pushed aside most of the time and then patted on the head when we get in a jam and need something in a hurry.

You boys should think about things like that. You know, there's another generation coming along right behind you; and with those new space machines and everything—

Is it that late already? I hadn't realized it. Well, I know you're anxious to blast off again. Now, be sure and fasten yourselves in properly. I've read that there's been a lot of accidents lately due to carelessness. And when you get up there I want you to remember to stay on course, and watch out for meteors, and be careful about denting the rocket fins when you set it down. And I hope you won't be staying out till all weeks of the year. Why, in my day—

All right, never mind.

Anybody seen what happened to my good old pipe?

"It's A Nice Trick But It Has No Significance"

HERBLOCK
©1957 THE WASHINGTON POST CO.

10/11/57

8/28/57

"Whew! At First I Thought It Was Sent Up By One Of The Other Services"

11/22/57

Moonglow

10/15/57

"That Ain't My Style," Said Casey . . . And The Umpire Said, "Strike Two!"

10/10/57

Call To Prayer

HERBLOCK
©1957 THE WASHINGTON POST CO.

10/13/57

Chins Up

11/5/57

"Dear Boy, Where Have You Been Keeping Yourself?"

HERBLOCK
©1957 HERBERT L. BLOCK

11/9/57

"Say, In That Moonlight You Look Kind Of Attractive"

10/20/57

"Never Mind About Already Having A Book"

11/8/57

"It's Just A Matter Of Space"

11/10/57

"What I Really Want Is A Few Jars Of Instant Science"

2/10/58

"Brother, Let Me Tell You About Tortoises"

HERBLOCK
©1958 THE WASHINGTON POST CO.

4/13/58

Fireside Chat

12/23/57

"Never Mind About Trees And Soil—Make Us Some Fruit"

1/8/58

"You Were Saying—?"

1/7/58

"—This Splendid Achievement, Made Possible By A Man Whose Name I Forget—"

8/13/58

3/27/58

"I Think I'll Orbit Over To The Army-Navy Club"

3/18/58

On the first successful launching of a Navy satellite

"Could You Put An Alarm Clock In The Next One?"

5/19/58

"Hey—Don't Forget The Bottom Part, Too"

11/13/57

"Be Sure To Give Mine Special Attention"

11/23/55

"What Year Are We In Now?"

12/27/56

"Ain't We Something!"

2/19/57

"Tell You What—We'll Help Some Of You Go On To Overcrowded Colleges"

12/31/57

"Fine—Now All We Need To Do Is Jack It Up And Put A School Under It"

1/28/58

"Think We'll Ever Get Up To 1958 Recession Levels?"

4/22/58

"This Happened Without Any Violence At All"

10/14/57

"Quiet! We're Thinking Up A New Reason"

3/25/58

"Now, Would You Mind Raising Your Little Finger?"

8/1/58

110

"It's Time To Get Into My Roomier-Than-Ever Car And Get The Kids At The More-Crowded-Than-Ever School"

5/10/57

"Don't You Ever Have Anything Fresh?"

HERBLOCK
©1958 THE WASHINGTON POST CO.

1/5/58

6

GLOBE-TROTTING

It isn't possible to do even a brief preface to a collection of cartoons on international matters without talking about a man who keeps turning up in them—John Foster Dulles. In making this agonizing appraisal, I'll merely say at the start that despite some less than flattering characterizations of him, I do not lay the blame for all the troubles of the world at Mr. Dulles' doorstep. And it wouldn't do much good if I did. That's the last place he'd be likely to see it. He gets around quite a bit, that man.

For several years I've been doing a lot of vicarious traveling with Mr. Dulles. I've followed, in the news columns and on TV, the flights on which he's shipped himself east and west of Suez, where the best-touted policies have seemed like the worst. I've also followed his flights of fancy through several magazine articles. The latter have been pretty remarkable. I've never known of anyone who had such a knack for turning defeats into victories with just a few deft phrases and a rose-tinted rear-view mirror.

I've been impressed by the Dulles agility and endurance as he has leaped from crisis to crisis and from brink to brink, while carrying the whole State Department in his hat. I don't envy his job, which has been a tough one. It wouldn't have been easy even if he and the President had stayed at their desks, studying information and intelligence, and formulating policies. And with all that traveling and writing to do, and the optimistic statements to put out, there hasn't been time for some of the usual State Department chores. On some occasions there's scarcely been time to return from an area and issue a glowing report on it before it has blown up.

I used to wonder why it was that, with so much governmental energy expended on political public relations at home, we didn't seem to succeed in making a better impression abroad. Apparently Mr. Dulles did a little wondering about that too, because after the 1958 Russian announcement on suspension of nuclear tests he told a press conference that a dictatorship like Russia's had a great natural propaganda advantage over a government like ours. He wasn't exactly envious of such a system, and he assured his listeners of his preference for democracy. But he seemed to have a wistful feeling that if the cantankerous old world would just stand still and give him its undivided attention, everything would be all right.

It seemed to me that the trouble in this respect was not so much that the Russians had an Iron Curtain as that Mr. Dulles often acted as if we were—or should be—behind a soundproof curtain. I think the Dullesian public-relations talk and the kind of favorable world opinion we sought abroad were, as an old lawyer might say, mutually exclusive.

For example, statements that everything was under control, which sounded so good over here, could not have sounded so good to allies that saw the Middle East slipping away and their oil sources threatening to go down the drain with it. I don't think they were so impressed as some over here by the ballyhoo about the Eisenhower Doctrine. And they could not all have shared Mr. Dulles' pride in pacts. Signing up a few governments on the dotted line did not—as we discovered in the Middle East—mean that the dotted boundary lines on maps would be sufficient to hold back revolutionary change.

Boasts about our tremendous power must have gone over with some irony in countries that wanted to see wiser use or better evidence of that power. Administration statements that our prestige in the world was never higher must have sounded odd to people in other parts of the world who knew much better than we did how we rated with them. And to impoverished people overseas, who were without the latest automobiles and home gadgets, the moralizings and all's-well statements that somebody once described as "candied comment" must have had a somewhat bitter taste.

A 1957 magazine article by Mr. Dulles telling us to demonstrate freedom at home and abroad sounded a little odd even over here, where Mr. Dulles was engaged in trying to curtail the freedom of people at home to *go* abroad.

In other articles and interviews he explained how shrewdly he manipulated international situations and statesmen. It might have been better if he had been a little less clever and more candid, or if he had been clever enough to leave the stories of his shrewdness for a book of memoirs. I guess it's a quantitative matter. It's often seemed that his cleverness was not in just the right amount—a little too much to win friends and not enough to outmaneuver our enemies. In any case, we haven't seemed to score heavily in the world through the practice of what probably should be called statementship—or through the issuance of status quotes.

Mr. Dulles is certainly a learned and experienced man. And I guess he can rattle off treaties and policies all the way back—although, the way things move these days, even good policies of a decade ago seem to get tired and run down.

But Mr. Dulles doesn't. He keeps going at a great clip and has frequently traveled tremendous distances to sit tight. I wish he'd rest himself a little more and start some fresh ideas moving around. Boy, can *those* things travel!

"Throw Another Log On The Fire"

"Now Is Everything Perfectly Clear?"

10/30/55

2/26/56

"Say—What Have We Got In This Next Race?"

"Just Let Me Catch Some Soldiers Moving In Here"

11/18/55

2/23/56

"Don't Be Afraid—I Can Always Pull You Back"

1/14/56

"Ah, That Good Old Sunshine"

3/18/56

"If He Shoots You, Let Me Know At Once"

4/11/56

"Oh, We're Getting A Picture Of The U. S., All Right"

6/22/56

"Fellows, I'm Neutral"

7/13/56

"Notice How We've Got Them Isolated?"

6/2/57

"You May Approach And Speak"

8/30/56

"Anything In Sight Yet?"

9/11/56

"Hang Your Clothes On A Hickory Limb But Don't Go Near The Brink"

9/14/56

Alarm

11/15/56

119

"It Came From Out Of Nowhere"

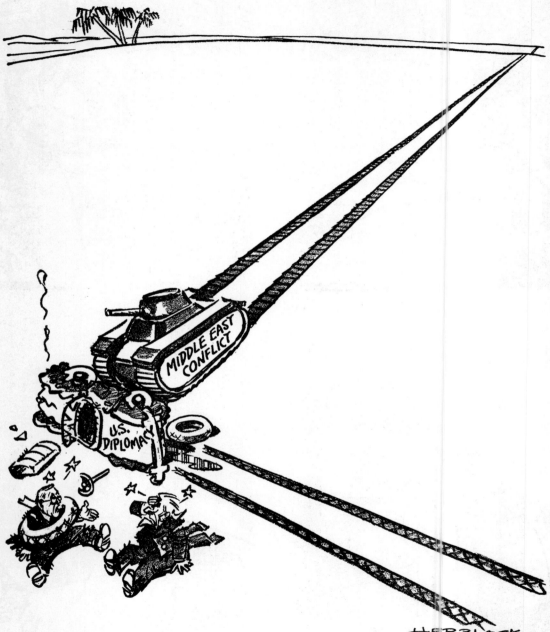

HERBLOCK
© 1956 THE WASHINGTON POST Co.

11/2/56

"Freezing To Death Isn't So Good Either"

11/29/56

"This Time Let's Get A New Tire"

11/14/56

"Oh, You Mean *That* Salvage Job"

12/19/56

"I Demand Sanctions"

2/27/57

2/10/57

"You Fellows Aren't Going To Put It Back Just Like That, Are You?"

"Say, What If She Doesn't Want Her Honor Protected?"

1/8/57

"No More Tranquilizers?"

1/17/57

"I Said, 'How Dare You Have Weapons Like That!'"

4/9/57

10/16/56

"It's Easier If You Keep Your Eyes Closed"

5/8/57

"Okay—Now Scram"

3/12/57

"I Haven't Laid A Hand On Her"

3/20/57

"Do You Think We've Gotten Any Closer?"

3/26/57

"You'll Find I'm Not Just Thinking Of Egypt"

4/26/57

"My, What Lovely C-H-I-N-A"

3/11/57

Whence All But He Had Fled

6/10/57

"Mr. Stassen Will Now Explain Our Position"

5/23/57

"Yeah—I'm Still In"

1/9/58

"We Can Sure Do Some Liberating Over Here"

12/2/56

"Out, Damned Spot! Out, I Say!"

9/11/57

"You See—Propaganda Everywhere"

4/19/57

"Stop At Once, Do You Hear?"

4/18/58

"Let Me Know When You Decide Something"

HERBLOCK
©1957 THE WASHINGTON POST CO.

4/24/57

"While You're Talking, I'll Bring Some More Chairs"

5/26/57

"What Say We Stand Up And Take That First Step?"

6/23/57

"When Do You Think The Preliminaries Will Be Over?"

7/1/57

"What About The Problems Of Inner Space?"

9/3/57

"And Now, Direct From 24 Weeks In London—"

9/9/57

"What Do I Hitch My Wagon To?"

11/24/57

"This Isn't A Push-Button Operation"

12/24/57

"You Think This Nuclear Stuff Really Produces Changes In People?"

4/1/58

132

5/25/57

"Couldn't We Get Ahead Of Them Some Time?"

8/23/57

"This Will Keep Out Foreign Salesmen"

2/21/58

"A Couple Of Holes In The Bottom Won't Even Show"

8/16/57

"Fellows, I'd Rather Stand On My Own Feet"

4/11/57

"Why Don't You Look Where You're Going?"

8/30/57

"Now, In This Case, We Recognize The Government But We Don't See The Machine Gun"

3/16/57

"We Got Another Room Ready?"

3/14/58

"I've Always Meant To Ask You, Juan— How Did You Make Out In This Business?"

1/21/58

"By The Way, What Have We Been Doing About Latin America These Past Few Years?"

5/14/58

"Betcha We Get This One Perfected First"

6/14/57

"Button, Button, Who Gets The Button?"

11/21/57

"Want Any More Arguments For Nuclear Control?"

5/18/58

Man On Horseback

6/11/58

"Have To Keep Peace In The Family, You Know"

6/8/58

"He May Not Be Doing So Well In California, But—"

6/13/58

"Well, I See Harold Got Him To Swallow Something"

2/5/58

"You Don't Understand Us Arabs"

10/28/57

"Never Laid A Glove On Me. By The Way, Where Am I?"

12/20/57

"Hurry! We Can Talk About Where We're Going After We Get There"

3/12/58

"When Do We Get Out Of This Depression?"

4/8/58

4/16/58

"Ev'rybody, Now—In The Good Old Summit Time, In The Good Old Summit Time—"

HERBLOCK
©1958 THE WASHINGTON POST CO.

1/30/58

"Your Office Seems To Be On Fire"

HERBLOCK
©1958 THE WASHINGTON POST CO.

5/27/58

"Nah—Wrong Kind Of Summit"

5/1/58

"Stay Right Where You Are—I'll Come To You"

7/25/58

Thinker

7/30/58

"Up?"

7/23/58

"As I Was Saying, We're Not Going To Lose Our Shirt"

HERBLOCK
©1958 THE WASHINGTON POST CO.

4/2/58

"I'll Be Glad To Come!—And I'll Set The Date, Make Up The
Guest List, Select The Program, Choose The Menu,
Pick Out The Music . . ."

7/24/58

"... At Night, When You're Asleep, Into Your Tent I'll Creep ..."

7/27/58

"I Can Lick Any Other Peace-Lover In The House"

HERBLOCK
©1958 THE WASHINGTON POST Co.

7/31/58

"Goodness Knows I Tried"

8/6/58

Convoy

9/16/58

148

"It Worked Fine As Long As Nobody Asked, 'Or Else What?' "

8/27/58

"Ah, But We Can't Fix It Now—It's Raining Again"

8/29/58

"You Can Make It"

8/22/58

"Very Simple—We Won't Recognize Their Bombs"

9/2/58

7

TOGETHERNESS

I FOLLOW the ads and commercials pretty closely. I guess I should say that they follow me. They surround me. Anyhow, I see them all the time. And I think I've spotted a general drift in them: The trend is toward trends.

They don't go so much any more for lines like, "Amaze your friends!" or "You can have something different!" They say, "The Swing Is To GRUNCHES!" or "EVERYBODY'S Using SLURGE!"

The advertisers have a word for it, and it's one that probably would have made the Greeks wince. The big word lately has been "togetherness." And even where all the consumers are not united in the joyful sharing of some product, the ads show landslide majorities in testimonials. Like "Eight Out Of Ten Unidentified Authorities Recommend Hicost Breadpills!"

We no longer see the old toothpaste ad warning of the dangers of pyorrhea with the words, "Four Out Of Five Have It." And it's just possible that in an age of conformity and togetherness the fifth guy got to feeling that whatever the other four had, he'd better have too. He probably said to hell with the toothpaste and went out and got himself a case of pyorrhea.

Well, togetherness has become quite a thing in politics, also—particularly on Capitol Hill, where some Congressional leaders have often seemed obsessed by a fear of sharp issues. And whenever members of both parties stand together—or lie down on the job together—somebody is going to notice how nicely they're getting along and say, "This is real statesmanship."

I don't want to seem like a surly fellow, but I think this kind of thing can be overdone. Bipartisanship can be a dandy thing, and I wouldn't be the one to spur partisans to general bloodletting for the pure joy of clouting each other around. But I think there's something to be said for apartness, particularly when the rest of the boys are toasting their togetherness with sleeping potions.

I've never seen much statesmanship in the kind of all-round hand-holding that leaves nobody in there pitching for the public interest. And if the urge to merge represented the acme of responsibility, there wouldn't be much point in having a two-party system—or an independent press. The alternative to the irresponsibility of reckless charges is not the irresponsibility of silence or acquiescence when somebody ought to be raising a good loud holler.

For example, in 1955 the Administration reluctantly went along with Congress in setting up an executive-legislative-Republican-Democratic commission to look into the internal-security program. That sounded like a plan for the biggest and best kind of get-together, which would leave no problems at all, except minor matters like who was going to bring the olives and pickles and who was going to bake the cake.

This "statesmanlike" move resulted in the eventual creation of an undistinguished commission, which finally turned in a mishmash report, which was soon forgotten. Nothing was accomplished except that a national problem had been swept under the rug.

The expressed purpose of the Democratic Congressmen who had conceived this idea was to "take security out of politics," and nothing could have seemed more laudable. But it might have been more to the point if they had demanded that politics be taken out of security, and that men who mixed politics and security be taken out of public office. That's the kind of thing an opposition party is supposed to do.

The Congressional unity and harmony are generally thickest in the closing hours of a session, when the legislators sing "Auld Lang Syne" and pass, "with a whoop and a holler," bills that sound terribly patriotic, but which are often merely terrible.

When sloppy bills, tied with red-white-and-blue ribbons, are brought up at the last minute, the "ayes" may be shouted with a noticeable twang, owing to the fact that some of the Congressmen are holding their noses at the time. But few would venture into a campaign without approving such measures, even though they may not have the slightest idea what's in them.

The same general principle applies to the almost unanimous support of reckless committees. For years there have been proposals for codes of ethics to govern such committees. And under Congresses both Democratic and Republican, these proposals have been pigeonholed and finally slid into the Potomac with nary a splash. Sometimes the bipartisanship outruns the ethics.

I can do with a lot less of the kind of togetherness in which political expediency makes strange under-the-bedfellows.

Newspapermen have sometimes been moved to speculate about other interesting examples of bipartisanship in inaction.

"Code Of Ethics? Why, Yes, I Believe There Was Some Talk Of One"

7/19/56

"Sweetiepie, Tell Us Little Old Judges In Your Own Words What A Scoundrel That Reuther Is"

3/20/58

"Howdy, Pardners"

5/29/58

"What Would It Cost To Add A Storm Cellar?"

3/30/58

Harry Ashmore of *The Arkansas Gazette* wrote a magazine article in the spring of 1958 in which he discussed what he said "must have been one of the most singular political deals in recent years." Said Mr. Ashmore:

> The new Attorney General, William P. Rogers, said that there were no present plans for further legal action in Little Rock. He further noted that the Administration would not press for additional civil-rights legislation at this session of Congress—a matter of some moment since the Justice Dept. had previously used as an excuse for inaction at Little Rock the failure of the enforcement provisions in the last civil rights bill.
>
> These pronouncements were followed by one of the most remarkable scenes enacted on Capitol Hill since the passage of the Missouri Compromise.
>
> Mr. Rogers appeared before the Senate Judiciary Committee to be interrogated as to his fitness as Attorney General, received cordial greetings, and was recommended for confirmation without a single question being addressed to him regarding his past or future course in the Little Rock case—and this before a committee that counts among its members Senators James Eastland of Mississippi and Olin Johnston of South Carolina.

Mr. Rogers was approved unanimously, and men like Mr. Ashmore were left to ponder the wondrous kinds of harmony that are pitched so high they are not audible to the human ear.

Most of the more interesting types of political togetherness are created by outside pressure; and probably the greatest political homogenizer of all is oil. The pressure of oil is strong enough to gush across party lines—and even to reach states that have little to do with oil production.

Both parties were distressed in 1956 when some pretty crude oil shot right up on the Senate floor and splashed into newspaper headlines, with the revelation of the activities of some overeager lobbyists.

Under discussion at the time was a bill to curtail federal regulation of gas companies. And while Senator Paul Douglas and a very few others fought a losing fight against the measure, most senators surveyed their fingernails and waited for the roll call that would put it over.

At that point, Senator Francis Case rose and disclosed that an oil lobbyist had tried to press upon him the sum of $2,500 as a sort of token of appreciation for his voting perspicacity.

This touched off a great deal of public indignation. It also aroused some indignation among some of the Senator's colleagues. How could he be so

"I've Told You Fifty Times—Not At The Front Door!"

HERBLOCK
©1958 THE WASHINGTON POST CO.

2/12/58

uncouth as to mention the matter at all, particularly when one of the oil lobby's pet bills was about to be voted on? Really, there were some members who just didn't seem to know how to behave in a gentleman's club.

The Senate rose above this unfortunate incident and passed the gas bill anyhow. But, in that campaign year, President Eisenhower sadly vetoed it because of the circumstances involved. At the same time, he invited another try.

Do you ever have times when everything seems to go wrong? The oil interests seldom do. But with the gas bill, they twice had the measure ready to slide through Congress and twice slipped on their own grease.

In 1958 the togetherness was complete. The oilmen wanted the bill. The President wanted the bill. The Congressional leaders wanted the bill. Most of the legislators were ready to okay it. And the head of the Federal Power Commission (supposedly an independent regulatory agency) spoke publicly for it. And then another story exploded.

Reporter Edward T. Folliard of the Washington *Post* disclosed the contents of a letter by Republican National Committeeman Jack Porter, inviting a number of well-heeled Texas tycoons to a dinner for Minority Leader Joe Martin. The gist of this invitation was that now was the time for good oilmen to come to aid of the party—at $100 a plate—to show their "appreciation" for Mr. Martin's special legislative services to the industry. The $100,000 which that dinner produced turned out to be "made in Texas for Texans," because the Republican National Committee, after anguished deliberation, decided that it was too hot to handle and left it with the state committee. The gas bill was put aside for another time.

"The Case case" aroused a public demand for investigation of the influence of powerful groups like the oil lobby, and for the reform of laws regulating political spending. And in response to popular request, as you might say, a perspiring Senate decided that committees should take a look into these matters—preferably a long, long look.

A committee headed by Senator John L. McClellan undertook an investigation of *all* lobbying influences, which gave it a chance to operate with the broadest possible lassitude.

The chairman issued a general invitation to his fellow legislators to drop in some time and tell him about improper influences upon them. This was a method of exposure somewhat different from that usually employed in Senate investigations, including others which starred Senator McClellan himself. For some reason, the Senator's office was not filled with colleagues and lobbyists elbowing and jostling each other to tell all; and the interesting new investigative technique produced no revelations.

One thing about that particular McClellan committee—it couldn't be

"Don't Be Naïve—That Was When I Was Sick"

HERBLOCK
©1956 THE WASHINGTON POST CO.

6/30/56

156

"Nice Little Kitty" "Want A Lift?"

12/3/56 1/23/56

charged with any excesses. It was characterized by such restraint that it's difficult to recall just when its work ended—or, for that matter, when it ever began.

The committee on political spending, headed by Senator Albert Gore, was something else again. After an investigation of the 1956 elections, this group declared it to be imperative that Congress act to revise the laws on political contributions. It pointed out that $33,000,000 of campaign spending had been reported in 1956, but that actual spending far exceeded that amount. And it said that the existing laws were so "hopelessly inadequate" and so "studded with loopholes" that it was impossible to calculate the actual total. Even more significantly, it showed that most of the political contributions came from sources comprising only a tiny fraction of the population.

The report called for limitation of political contributions by individuals, for broader-based political participation and less "private subsidization." With togetherness all the rage, it might be supposed that such all-embracing proposals would have a big appeal for the legislators. But they realize that there must be moderation in all things. When you get together a few special interests, the executive department and a lot of Congressmen of both

6/25/56   2/5/57

parties, that makes quite a crowd, right there. You just can't carry these
things to a point where they get out of hand.

At the time, Senate Majority Leader Lyndon Johnson of Texas predicted
that Congress would act on "a comprehensive revision of the election laws."
But the Senate Majority Leader is a very busy man, with a lot of things
on his mind. And he couldn't be expected to remember proposals like that,
especially after the furor had died down.

Senators Gore, Hennings and a few others advanced political-campaign-
reform proposals, which were taken under solemn deliberation—to a depth
of about six feet. There are times when even the most loquacious legislators
get to feeling that silence is indeed golden.

What was the final score on the Case affair, which created such a flurry
at the time? Two oil lobbyists, Neff and Patman, stood trial and were fined
$2,500 apiece. Since, by a curious irony, each was called upon to pay the
exact amount that the two had tried to give away to one senator, it could
hardly be said that the interests they represented had suffered a mortal blow.

Through good times and bad times, the oil companies have received special benefits from the government, including the "depletion allowance"
which permits them to deduct 27½ per cent of their gross income before taxes.

4/10/58

The amount of money lost to the U.S. Treasury through this allowance alone runs to hundreds of millions of dollars a year.

During a period when the government seemed to be counting its pennies and when children were kept out of better schooling to learn the value of a budget dollar, you might think that the loss of all this revenue would have put the President and the Congress and the Secretary of the Treasury into a state of depression—if I may turn a phrase—that would curl their hair. But it didn't and doesn't. The hairs of most of these gentlemen, including some with more hair to curl than Mr. Eisenhower and former Secretary Humphrey, remained as smooth and unruffled as if they were slicked down with petroleum jelly. Unlike his predecessor in the White House, President Eisenhower made no fight to reduce such special privileges.

An effort to do this was made, in 1957, by a small group of senators including Senator Douglas (Dem.) and Senator Williams (Rep.). But there was no noticeable big swing in their direction. In fact, most senators literally could not be budged from their seats. With appeals to both sides of the aisle, the Douglases and Williamses were not even able to muster enough support to require a record vote which would have obliged their colleagues to stand up and be counted.

Such general concern for a fabulously rich and powerful industry is indeed touching—especially in the pocketbook of the small taxpayers, who make up such revenue losses and who receive no special "production incentives" other than occasional nudges from installment collectors.

A few people, in and out of Congress, have worked persistently to break the charmed circle of "togetherness," in which government, through special tax concessions, in effect subsidizes special interests to increase their pressures on government. But most Congressmen and most members of the present executive department have seemed happy to gaze into each other's eyes and murmur, "This thing is bigger than both of us." And as long as the campaign contributions roll in and the special benefits roll out, everyone seems to be happy—except those advocates of apartness who believe that no special interest should be bigger than the government of the United States.

Many pressure groups have labored to keep people from seeing the interests of the entire country. But one group has worked hard to keep us from seeing much of the country itself. The billboard lobby has been what might be called a special-interest groups' special-interest group, supported by many corporations which would literally put their products before the beauties of nature. These have included, naturally enough, the oil companies—because why should a motorist be looking at the scenery when he can be reading, all along the way, about some wonderful product on which he can gas up at the next pump?

During 1957 and 1958 the billboard lobby—with assistance even from some labor unions—fought energetically against any regulation of roadside eye-

"You Can Still Buy Picture Postcards Of The Scenery"

HERBLOCK
©1957 THE WASHINGTON POST CO.

8/25/57

"Anyone Care About Old-Fashioned Open Space?"

sores in the planned 41,000-mile federal highway program. Oil-rich Senator Kerr ridiculed as "assthetes" those crazy dreamers who thought that when the people rolled out $35,000,000,000 for a federal highway program, they had a right to enjoy the view of their country.

But on this issue, which was, so to speak, plain as a billposter, men with the inside track found themselves surrounded by a larger circle of Americans. Senator Richard Neuberger (Dem.) aided by Senator Thomas H. Kuchel (Rep.) rallied the millions of people who belonged to motor clubs, garden clubs, and no organizations at all. And they let out a scream which could be heard above the sweet-and-low harmonizings of legislators and high-octane lobbyists. There was finally inserted in the 1958 highway bill a modest provision that would give individual states some small federal financial incentive to curb billboards along the new U.S. highway. And if the people keep at it, they can bring those state governments to share the same public—and scenic—views.

Now, that kind of togetherness I don't mind at all. In fact, I'm willing to toast it with whatever yummy beverage is currently being featured—provided, of course, that it's not being plugged on some billboard that defaces a pleasant scene. A few more little victories like that could even serve to advertise a political trend, so that he who runs for office may read, "The Swing Is To John W. Public."

"If We're Gonna Have 'Em, We Might As Well Use 'Em"

7/28/57

"Shaddup!—You're Just The Guy That's Paying For This Car"

3/11/58

163

"Where IS Everybody?"

HERBLOCK
©1956 THE WASHINGTON POST CO.

1/26/56

"All Ready For The Parade, Children?"

1/27/56

"Maybe They Can't Find Anyone Who Can Be Cleared"

10/14/55

"All Right, You Guys—Line Up"

2/12/56

"I'm Strictly A Budget-Cutter, Mister"

6/16/57

"We Don't Want To Leave Any Stone Unturned"

HERBLOCK
©1956 THE WASHINGTON POST CO.

2/16/56

"You Fellows Haven't Seen Any Undue Influence Around Here, Have You?"

12/20/56

"Ain't No Oil Lobby Here, Jack. We're All Educators"

6/17/56

"Good Work—By The Way, Did You Find Anyone On The Roof Garden?"

3/1/57

"Think It's Really One Of Those Two-Stage Jobs?"

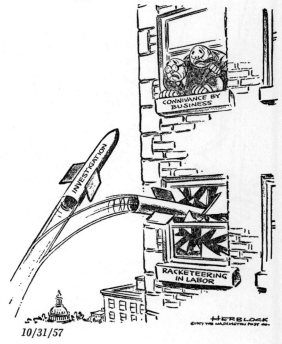

10/31/57

"They Don't Like To Be Disturbed"

HERBLOCK
©1957 THE WASHINGTON POST CO.

2/17/57

"You Got Elected, Didn't You?"

2/8/57

"Watch Closely, Now"

9/7/56

"Tell The Peasants To Step Aside"

2/3/58

"Now We'll See Which Of Us Talked Louder"

2/6/56

169

5/31/57

"The Rank And File Are Right Behind Me"

9/27/57

Memory Lane

8/27/57

"I Wouldn't Let You Use This Old Thing—It Might Not Give You Enough Protection"

8/21/58

"You Should Have Done Better Than That"

8/24/58

172

8

FINANCIAL AND ECONOMIC REPORT

I DON'T KNOW what there is about automatic elevators that brings out all the insecurity and pessimism in people; but they have that effect. We have such elevators in the building in which I work, and I've seen what happens. It's not just that little old ladies beseech me to accompany them from the second floor to the fourth. Big, strong, confident men who want to go UP almost invariably peer into the crowded elevator when it stops and ask hopelessly, "Down?" And vice versa. They just don't believe they can win on one of those things.

I have much the same feeling about the stock market. I'm certain that if I have a couple of shares of Drainboard Common and sell them, the market will thereupon go up like a three-stage rocket; and that if I buy a couple of shares of Dynamic Cereals, the market will immediately plunge deeper than a bathosphere. If anyone wanted to back me, I'm sure that I could, in this strange reverse way, make Wall Street perform like a yo-yo.

As for economics and finance in general, I do not try to pit myself against the experts who write long pieces on these subjects. I frequently get lost between the carloadings and the inventories and fail to catch their conclusions at all. But I am at one with them when they describe a situation or a trend as "uncertain." That is where I put my palms on the table, lean forward, and say, "Gentlemen, you have read my mind."

With the federal budget it's a little different. This gets out of the field of prophecy and into something pretty substantial. I do not profess to know it backward-and-forward or in-and-out; but I have a general idea of up and down. And on at least one occasion a governmental hassle over this subject made me feel like a veritable tower of strength. That was in 1957, when

"Whatsamatter—You Retiring From Practice?"

HERBLOCK
©1957 THE WASHINGTON POST CO,

11/15/57

President Eisenhower presented a record budget—and, in effect, asked Congress to cut it.

I may not know which way the elevator is going, but I know which way I want it to go. I don't ask for up and down both at the same time; and I don't press the *down* button when I want *up*. And, for that matter, most people who present government budgets don't, either. But in this case there were evidently divided counsels, and the news accounts probably should have been headed "Budget Cuts Administration."

As far as inflation, deflation, recession, budgets, and things of that sort are concerned, I have a few positive views which I'll be happy to set down, with no encouragement other than the fact that we've both got this far.

For one thing, I think that when individuals or organizations find they have a chance to pile up some real gravy and hear that we should all give thought to the long-range welfare of the entire economy, they seldom say, "Gee—I guess I'll let the extra money go."

And I feel strongly that when recessions are ended, it is not because those same individuals or groups have been told to *SPEND!* During the Hoover Administration there was an antihoarding commission of some kind, and I recall seeing signs in the streetcars and buses telling us not to hoard our money. Those reminders had an effect that was absolutely electrifying. At every corner, people were jumping off to run home and put some extra hemstitching into the mattresses that contained what was left of their savings.

I also have a definite feeling that a government budget, based on needs and reasonably flexible taxation and financing, is not quite the same thing as a family budget, which is based on a fixed pay check. And it's my impression that a lot of the people who try to tell us the national budget is exactly like a little old family budget are sufficiently affluent that they do not have to operate on tight little old family budgets.

And one more thing: When a political candidate says that he is going to slash the budget, cut taxes, and at the same time provide for all necessary public needs, the correct answer is "Uh huh."

I guess that's about all for now. So long. Don't take any wooden slogans.

"Pay No Attention To Rover. He Just Likes To Join In"

12/7/56

"Darn Good Speech But I Didn't Catch All Of It"

1/13/57

"You'd Think They'd Synchronize Them Some Way"

1/22/57

"Who's Ahead?"

4/8/57

The Prodigal Father

5/9/57

"Who Gave Him The Do-It-Yourself Kit?"

HERBLOCK
©1957 THE WASHINGTON POST CO.

3/31/57

178

"Couldn't You Distribute It A Little Better?"

5/21/56

"I Can Do It For You Wholesale"

7/17/56

"And With The One That Can Blow Up The Entire World We Get Trading Stamps"

5/7/57

"Let Joy Be Unconfirmed"

12/21/55

"Careful You Don't Get Yourself Down"

8/18/55

"I'm Fine. Of Course, Every Once In A While I Go Like This—"

2/13/57

"Now How Do I Keep The Goose That Lays The Golden Eggs From Killing Me?"

7/17/57

"And We Have Also Saved Money, Dear Friends, By Eliminating Flood Insurance Funds"

6/20/57

"Boys—Please—Are You Listening To Me?"

6/30/57

"It's Not That We Like You Less—"

7/11/57

"The Drifting Of The Boat Caused The Anchor To Rise"

8/11/57

"Oh, We Think Of This As Just A Launching Platform"

10/24/57

"Oh, Great!—That's All I Needed"

8/5/58

"You Sure You've Got This Hitched Up Right?"

9/12/57

"I'm Trying Not To"

9/8/57

"What Are We Fighting Now—Inflation Or Deflation?"

11/19/57

"Boy, These New Cars Will Do Anything"

12/26/57

"How Many Are Now—Uh—Temporarily Inactive In The—Uh—Economic Readjustment?"

2/7/58

"Well, I Got That In, All Right"

HERBLOCK
©1958 THE WASHINGTON POST CO.

1/14/58

"Or Maybe You'd Rather Put In A New Floor"

1/16/58

"What Is It We're Trying To Save?"

3/2/58

Different Worlds

1/15/58

"Can't Be Spending Money Foolishly, You Know"

3/4/58

"I Hear We're In A—Puff Puff—Breathing Spell"

2/11/58

"Let's Face This Squarely—Some Of You Haven't Been Smiling Enough"

2/23/58

"Mind If We Play Through?"

3/10/58

3/21/58

"Don't Get Hysterical—I'm Watching All The Time"

4/24/58

"You Know, I Think People Are Worrying Less About The Recession"

5/20/58

"Couldn't Have Happened At A Better Time"

3/8/58

"Man, This Is Certainly A Good Joke On The Union"

5/5/58

"Is That The Height Of Our Ambition?"

5/4/58

"My Boy, Have You Thought Of Continuing With A Graduate Course?"

6/1/58

"Who—Me? I Can't Afford To"

6/6/58

"Yes, It's—Ulp—Delicious"

8/3/58

"It's Great How Things Are Picking Up"

9/1/58

9

IN PURSUIT OF THE LAW

IT WAS probably about the time when "sophisticated westerns" were being introduced that I came across a news item which told of strange cries and confusion at the showing of a horse opera in a London movie house. The confusion resulted from the fact that the good guys were not all wearing white hats and the bad guys were not all wearing black hats. In the fast sequences, particularly, the moviegoers kept finding themselves cheering for the wrong fellows. This was quite an unnerving experience, and they left the theater badly shaken. Some of them even wrote letters to the *Times*.

I was so struck by the story that I used it as a text for a 1956 talk on government investigations and blacklisting. The general idea was that things were not so simple as they were in the old-fashioned movies when the good guys were clearly good, the bad guys were clearly bad, and everything was black and white, including the costumes.

It seemed to me that many people in our own country had gone through a similar experience in watching the wide-screen national scene. Over a period of years, a lot of them had been discovering that anyone who figuratively put on a white hat, or a red-white-and-blue hat, and wrapped himself in the American flag was not necessarily a hero. And some of the men who had announced that they were hot after subversive varmints had even turned out to be king-size varmints themselves.

Since the time of those observations, however, the professional hunters of subversion have acted to simplify things for us so that we can follow the action more easily, even if we can't follow the logic. They have found a convenient and easily identifiable set of villains, complete with black costumes —the little band of robed men who hang out in the United States Supreme Court Building.

"Pardon Me, But I Think That's My Hat"

HERBLOCK
©1956 THE WASHINGTON POST CO.

7/4/56

In this western—which is really more of an eastern—the pursuers do not have a common uniform and some of them must be a little uncomfortable in the company of other pursuers in white nightshirts. Each hard-riding character may have his own brand of 100-proof Americanism, but they all have scores to settle with Those Men In Black.

What I want to do here is to lope along, peering into the canyons and gulches where the professional pursuers of subversion gather, and catch glimpses of them at work protecting us from our rights.

Aside from the red-hot segregationists, one of the first groups to raise a cry against the court was a collection of state officials who objected to a 1956 decision on sedition.

The Court ruled that since Congress had acted in this field, the matter of what constituted sedition against the U.S. rested with the federal government and was not something to be determined in forty-eight or forty-nine different ways.

That seemed reasonable enough, even taking into account that what is plain sense is not *ipso facto* plain law. But it's easy to see how the various arbiters of "Americanism" felt it was cutting into their work. If every vigi-

"Have Fun, Kids"

"Well, Look Who Turned Out To Be The Masked Terror"

5/31/56

12/5/55

lante couldn't set himself up as an Uncle Sam this was a blow to Free Enterprise—that's what it was. And a fine how-do-you-do if the federal courts were going to bring law and order into the law-and-order business!

Surprisingly, this decision was also opposed by U.S. Attorney General Brownell, possibly feeling that he and the state attorneys general were all brothers in a great fraternity. But then he had his own complaints against the federal courts for frowning on some of his security-program procedures.

Some of the most direct attacks on the Supreme Court have come from a couple of Congressional committees which have made a career of pursuing publicity and whatever they choose to call "subversive influences"—the Senate Internal Security Subcommittee and the House Committee on Un-American Activities. Their reaction was understandable because they have for so long been operating as if they were courts that they have come to regard duly authorized judges as usurpers, if not impostors.

The Senate Internal Security Subcommittee is headed by James O. Eastland of Mississippi, where the internal security is not so good for most citizens who want to exercise the right to vote. It would not be putting it too strongly to say that Senator Eastland was most unhappy with the Supreme Court decision on integration. He urged defiance of it and tried to promote the idea that Communists were lurking under the federal bench.

The former chairman and ranking Republican on the committee was Senator William Jenner, probably best known for having out-McCarthied McCarthy by denouncing General George C. Marshall as a living lie and a front man for traitors.

Under these stalwart defenders of the American Way, the committee acted in 1956 to save us from the dangers of a free press. It summoned several past and present members of the staff of the New York *Times*, a newspaper which had been critical of the methods of the committee, and of Eastland and Jenner in particular. This "investigation" trailed off, with the committee mumbling that it really hadn't been investigating the press and wasn't trying to intimidate anybody at all.

In 1957 it thought of another novel way of looking after the internal security of the United States. It got its biggest publicity play of the year by rehashing six-year-old charges concerning E. H. Norman, then Canadian ambassador to Egypt. And it got an extra helping of headlines a few weeks later, when Mr. Norman committed suicide in Cairo.

Committee counsel Morris, who said that Mr. Norman's name "just happened to come up," had managed—by persistent effort—to bring it up, despite the protests of the U.S. State Department. Since those old charges were already known to both governments, it was difficult to see what good purpose was served by this action. It was even more difficult to see how our security was protected by antagonizing a friendly government to a point

"Time For Your Investigation Of The Press, Senator"

1/4/56

4/5/57   4/7/57

where it threatened to stop sharing information with us. But it was not hard to see the headlines. Of those there were aplenty, even though they proved to be of no help to Mr. Morris in his attempt to win nomination for public office.

In 1958 the committee's big deal in internal security was the reporting out of a bill, conceived by Senator Jenner, to strip the United States Supreme Court of its jurisdiction in six different areas. This would merely have thrown the federal judicial system into chaos.

For such services beyond and below the call of duty, this committee receives over $200,000 a year. In 1957 it collected $289,291.45, an odd sum. There was something intriguing about that extra 45 cents. It might have represented the cost of a taxi to follow some fellow traveler who was going only a short distance. It might have been the price of a hot tip from some professional informant who needed a quick shot to stir his flagging memory. Perhaps it was the cost of a cheap basin for washing the hands. Or it might have represented the value which the U.S. Senate actually placed on the committee's work. I suppose we'll never know.

Now let us go from the fantastic to the ridiculous. On the other side of the

"I'll Have The Law On You"   **"Don't Ask Me Why—It's An Old Ritual"**

2/24/58   2/2/58

Capitol is the House Committee on Un-American Activities—which, in the same field, operates the oldest established floating political crap game in the country.

This committee has always had an affinity for spotlights, which has taken it many times to Hollywood and brought many Hollywood stars to Washington. It has also made several trips to New York, where it has laid some of the largest eggs in theatrical history. In 1957 it even tried a melodic performance, investigating un-Americanism in the world of music, but the press notices were discouraging, and that show folded after a very short run.

It was only natural that when Speaker Rayburn ruled against further televising of hearings by House committees, the loudest cry of anguish and defiance should have come from the chairman of this stage-struck committee —that old trouper of the subversive circuit, Francis Walter. But, true to tradition, he determined that the show must go on, even with the TV lights off.

Few things have aroused greater ire in Mr. Walter—whose ire is aroused rather easily—than the publication, in 1956, of a pair of books which represented an independent inquiry into the entertainment industry. These were

8/24/55   6/24/57

reports on blacklisting in movies and broadcasting, written by John Cogley, former editor of *Commonweal*.

Mr. Walter, who is the current keeper of the committee's granddaddy of all blacklists, asserted that there was no such thing as blacklisting. And he held hearings to prove it. He heard testimony from one of the authors of *Red Channels*, from the editor of an American Legion publication, and from others who list names and alleged associations in much the same manner as the committee itself. All such witnesses agreed that there were no blacklists; and one witness explained, without cracking a smile, that there were no lists at all—only files.

The witnesses and the committee also agreed that none of them had ever ever ever wanted to injure anyone; they were interested only in what they called "rehabilitation."

Let me give a little short course here on the blacklist—beg pardon, "rehabilitation"—work engaged in by these patriots. The committee might, for example, have included in its files a little card which said: *It's reported that a movie and television performer named Lassie was once seen running with a pack that contained a Russian wolfhound.*

If Lassie wanted to keep performing, she was supposed to come bounding in to the committee and say, "I was a dirty dog, a real hound. But now I have seen the dark and I'm repentant. I will promise to lie down or roll over whenever anyone barks at me. And thanks, fellows, for the splendid job you're doing."

If the committee was in a mellow mood, it might be content to make sneering remarks at Lassie and call her a prize dope. And if she was sufficiently grateful and obsequious before it, she might even be able to find employment again some day.

But if the committee chose to bear down it would insist on names. In that case, Lassie would be expected to say, "Rover and Spot and Rin-Tin-Tin were also dirty dogs and I hope you'll bite them too. And thanks again."

Among the many private citizens who were guilty of no crimes and had no knowledge of any, but who were nevertheless grilled by the committee in this manner, were John T. Watkins, labor-union organizer, and Arthur Miller, noted playwright. On grounds of conscience, they self-respectfully declined to play the Name Game and were cited for contempt.

The Watkins case reached the Supreme Court first; and when the contempt conviction was overruled, Mr. Walter became overwrought.

Now, contempt of Congress is nothing to be taken lightly, but it's not always as impressive as it sounds. The term suggests a group picture of an entire legislative body carefully deliberating charges presented by a committee after solemn deliberation. But that isn't quite the way it works.

An Eastland or a Jenner or a Walter gets his committee chairmanship through seniority, and confirmation by his colleagues is practically automatic. The counsel selected by a chairman is approved by the committee almost automatically. And when a committee, under their leadership, decides for such a citation, the Senate or House upholds it almost automatically.

On the part of the United States Congress as a whole, the processes behind a contempt citation usually involve all the deliberation, dignity, and decision of a penny slot machine rolling out balls of bubble gum.

What may have distressed Mr. Walter even more than the Watkins ruling itself was that part of the Court's decision which took a close look at the vague Congressional resolution which had established the committee. Wrote the Chief Justice: "It would be difficult to imagine a less explicit authorizing resolution. Who can define the meaning of 'un-American'?" That is an interesting question, and one that could come up again.

Congressman Walter's concepts of "un-American" behavior have been far-ranging. But in July 1958 he managed to outdo himself by finding the executive branch of the government guilty of recognizing the authority of the judicial branch. In a stern letter to Secretary of State Dulles, he accused Frances G. Knight, director of the Passport Office, of "going out of her way" to comply

"Why Should This Guy Have A Conscience When I Ain't Got One?"

2/22/57

200

"There Ain't No Blacklist—And You're In Contempt For Not Contributing Names To It"

"Neither Of You Fellows Heard About This?"

7/12/56

6/14/56

promptly with a ruling of the United States Supreme Court. And he demanded to know whether such actions were approved by the Secretary or whether they reflected "capricious and unauthorized action on her part."

This example of a dangerous tendency to obey Court decisions might have gone uncensured had it not been for the ever-alert chairman of the Committee on Un-American Activities.

There are a few members of another group of officials who have also cried havoc and seen the destruction of the Republic in civil-liberties rulings of the courts. Some policemen complain that their work is made more difficult by decisions upholding the rights of people arrested. This is sad but true.

It would unquestionably be easier for the John Laws if they were permitted to go at their work with gusto, beating down doors at random, hauling people away in trucks, and scaring hell out of them. The men who wrote the Bill of Rights were certainly aware of this. And they made sure that if a policeman's lot was to be a happier one, it would not be through methods which would make the lot of other citizens insufferable.

It is sometimes argued that the rights of society must be protected, as well as the rights of criminals. But the fact is that there are no specific "rights of society," "rights of criminals," "rights of Communists," "rights of non-Communists" or "rights of people with green hair." There is just one set of rights, and it belongs to each of the individuals who make up "society." What are sometimes referred to as the "rights of criminals" are the same rights which keep you and me from being whisked off and tossed into the clink for an indefinite stay, for having walked the dog some chilly night with our coat collars turned up.

When a convicted criminal is released as a result of a court decision, it is easy for police to cry that they are being "hamstrung by technicalities," or for demagogues to say that the courts are turning conspirators and murderers loose upon us. However, the fault in such cases usually lies not with the courts, but with sloppy police work or overzealous prosecutions that employ short cuts which would short-circuit the liberties of all of us.

It is one of the oddities of the time that while federal justices and their decisions have been denounced with reckless abandon, the statements and publicity releases of the federal police generally have been treated as reverently as if they were tablets handed down from a mountaintop.

In a column written in July 1957, Drew Pearson cited some examples of cases in which he said the FBI—and its chief—received more credit than was deserved. And he added quite candidly that no newspaperman, including himself, had published the complete truth in such cases.

Certainly this bureau has not been given the same careful scrutiny as others in government. And J. Edgar Hoover, particularly when he is delivering pronouncements on debatable subjects, could benefit from the kind of critical appraisal that is given such other public servants as, say, the President of the United States or the Chief Justice of the Supreme Court.

When the Administration security program came under criticism from a number of distinguished jurists, Mr. Hoover defended it in the most extravagant terms. In several speeches he strongly implied that anyone who criticized this program or disapproved of complete reliance on anonymous informers must be either a Communist or Communist dupe.

Mr. Hoover has performed some good work in his capacity as a policeman; but when he tried to get away with that kind of talk he got himself caught, as you might say, flat-footed. Happily, there were at least a few newspapers which said so, in editorials that did not support him in the manner to which he had become accustomed. This was a healthy reaction from members of a free press who should not have any sacred cows—or sacred bulls.

A 1958 statement by Mr. Hoover demanded tougher methods of dealing with juvenile delinquents and attacked a "distorted notion of justice" which he said had "even permeated our court system." This brought a rejoinder from Monsignor John O'Grady, secretary of the National Conference of Cath-

Prayer Rug

7/10/57

"Who Said A Policeman's Lot Is Not A Happy One?"

9/1/57

204

olic Charities, who found the statement shocking. Father O'Grady, who has had some experience in the social-welfare field, offered a contrary view. And he politely suggested that despite what he called Mr. Hoover's important contributions to police work, "This does not . . . entitle him to the position of an oracle in dealing with all questions of juvenile delinquency."

It might be added that Mr. Hoover also is not exactly our greatest authority on constitutional law, on what can properly be shown on movies and TV, on how to cope with Communism, or on a number of other subjects on which he has spoken in oracular fashion.

In the spring of 1958, Mr. Hoover and the Committee on Un-American Activities joined in doing some televiewing-with-alarm. The TV broadcast that brought screams from them was an interview—produced by the Fund for the Republic—with Cyrus Eaton, multimillionaire Cleveland industrialist.

A plain-spoken and unintimidated man—and one who, at seventy-five, was in no mood to learn any other kind of Americanism—Mr. Eaton had his say on a number of subjects, including foolish extremes of secrecy and spreading police activities. Speaking of the FBI, he said, in part:

"Boy, Am I Burning Up"

HERBLOCK
COPT THE WASHINGTON POST CO.

6/19/57

"Ha! An Un-American Tendency Toward Free Speech!"

HERBLOCK
©1958 THE WASHINGTON POST CO.

5/21/58

205

"All We Want Is The Truth As We See It"

6/16/58

I think it's had a tremendous buildup. It has enjoyed wonderful propaganda and sold itself in a marvelous way. But I always worry when I see a nation feel that it is coming to greatness through the activities of its policemen. And the FBI is just one of the scores of agencies in the United States engaged in investigating, in snooping, in informing, in creeping up on people . . .

Mr. Hoover delivered a blast clearly aimed at Mr. Eaton, but he declined the Fund's offer of equal TV time to reply. Time was demanded, however, by the Committee on Un-American Activities, which had not even been mentioned in the broadcast. And this request was quickly granted by executives of the network, who demonstrated that snoopers and informers were not the only ones who knew how to creep.

On this "reply" broadcast, the counsel for the committee announced that Mr. Eaton would be served with a subpoena. Both the committee and Mr. Hoover explained that they had nothing against free speech, mind you. The committee only wanted to make inquiries, and Mr. Hoover merely deplored "inaccuracies in the exercise of free speech." But the public reaction to the subpoena idea was not favorable, and the committee finally dropped the whole thing.

Mr. Hoover's imprecise speech exercises may be illustrated by an address he delivered to the 1957 national convention of the American Legion. Here he said, among other interesting things, that "certain organizations obviously dedicate their efforts to thwart the very concepts of security." He did not specify which organizations, or whose concepts of security they were trying to thwart. But he went on to say that "they vehemently oppose methods to gain this security and it is obvious that their aim is to destroy it."

He continued darkly, if somewhat vaguely, "They hypocritically bar communists from their membership but they seem to hate all persons who abhor communists and communism. They claim to be anticommunist but they launch attacks against Congressional legislation designed to curb communism."

Mr. Hoover had not yet let anyone in on the secret of what organizations he referred to, nor had he mentioned any methods or any legislation specifically. But the mystery cleared up in the next paragraph, in which he said, without elaboration: "The recent campaign to throw open the files of the FBI is a case in point."

At this point—or at this case in point—the cat was out of the bag on all four pussy feet, and we discovered the kind of dangerous subversives who were the objects of Mr. Hoover's creeping McCarthyism. First and foremost on anybody's list of "organizations" which would "throw open the files of the FBI," as Mr. Hoover misrepresented the matter, would have to be that

1/11/56   6/6/57

familiar group of desperadoes, the Supreme Court of the United States. And Mr. Hoover's tirade was brought on by their 7–1 decision which upheld the rights of people being prosecuted to see government material necessary for their defense—as, for example, the various conflicting statements of an informant like Harvey Matusow.

As one who believes that all government actions are subject to questioning and comment, I don't hold that federal court decisions are always right or above criticism. There are some I'd quarrel with. But in a choice, I'd certainly take the considered deliberations of the Supreme Court in preference to the statements of a policeman so carried away by his own power and his own press releases that he has taken to impugning the integrity and patriotism of all who disagree with him.

A more forthright crack at the Court appeared in a mid-1958 report of testimony by Mr. Hoover before a Congressional committee. He said, "The Supreme Court must come to grips in a realistic manner with facts and join all the forces for good in protecting society."

This was pretty big of our most publicized bureau chief. He might have said simply that the U.S. Supreme Court must go. But he was forbearing, though firm. He allowed the members of the nation's highest tribunal a chance to give themselves up and to "join all the forces for good."

Who knows to what heights men like Earl Warren and Hugo Black might have risen had they but obeyed and grasped the opportunity for redemption? They might have traded in their black robes for white hats, to show they were forces-for-good guys instead of forces-for-bad guys. They might even have become Junior G-men. But they remained steeped in their iniquities, steeped in the law, steeped in the old idea that the rights of American citizens are even more important than the barkings of cops and committees.

Actually, the law that has been operating against the Eastlands, the Jenners, the Walters and the Hoovers is one which has never been passed upon by the Supreme Court, and which appears not in legal books but in economic ones. That is the law of diminishing returns.

With all their combined efforts, they have not been able to keep the country's fears of internal "subversion" whipped up to the fever pitch of the McCarthy era. The Russian gains on world scientific, economic and political fronts have brought a sobering realization of the real dangers which confront us. And the Suspect-Thy-Neighbor groups have been up against the

"We're Agreed, Then—The Supreme Court Is Unconstitutional"

5/15/56

"You're Creating Chaos And Confusion And Hate!"

3/13/56

additional handicap that the strength of the Communists in the U.S., which was never large at any time, has dwindled to near zero.

In their efforts to overcome the law of diminishing returns, Mr. Walter and Mr. Hoover have tried to proclaim a kind of basic law of their own invention—that the fewer the Communists and the less their influence, the more imminent the danger from them.

If it were a fact that our internal peril is now as great as ever, that would hardly seem much of a testimonial to these men, who have supposedly been eliminating the dire threat that we're all going to turn red some morning. But in the face of clear and present dangers to their personal prestige, they could hardly be expected to worry about little matters of logic.

The business of hunting Americans guilty of no crimes and of finding "subversion" in such things as free speech and freedom of assembly is not yet played out. But the chases aren't what they used to be.

The pursuers are still willing, but the audience is getting tired. And, worst of all, the pursued aren't all co-operating in quite the old way. It takes at least two to make a chase. Somebody has to run away, or maybe drop dead when you point at him. But people aren't dropping the way they used to—or falling for all the old charges. As for running, the Supreme Court just sits there, handing down judicial opinions. People like Cyrus Eaton sit there handing out personal opinions; and instead of fleeing when a pursuer comes roaring up, they just stand and spit in his eye.

Perhaps Mr. Hoover has detected something in the air. Lately I've been reading lots of newspaper stories about an FBI list of Ten Most Wanted Men. This sounds like an echo of the old Public Enemy days when Mr. Hoover built his reputation by catching criminals, and by upholding the laws instead of trying to dictate them.

Jenner has bowed out. And if the business of pursuing law-abiding citizens keeps dropping off, I don't know what people like Eastland and Walter are going to do for action. Some time when they come up for new appropriations, Congress could suggest that they go chase themselves.

"I Got A Good Mind To Cut You Adrift"

HERBLOCK
© 195? THE WASHINGTON POST Co.

7/4/57

"That's A Laugh, Ain't It?"

HERBLOCK
©1956 THE WASHINGTON POST CO.

2/17/56

"I Guess I'd Better Start Throwing Some Weight Around, Too"

HERBLOCK
©1956 THE WASHINGTON POST CO.

5/20/56

"You Using A Pinch Of Salt In Your Recipe, Dearie?"

HERBLOCK
©1956 THE WASHINGTON POST CO.

5/17/56

"Grandma, I've Been Doing Some Wondering About You"

HERBLOCK
©1955 THE WASHINGTON POST CO.

11/27/55

"We'll Do All The Judging Around Here"

CONGRESSIONAL COMMITTEE "COURTS"

U.S. SUPREME COURT

HERBLOCK
©1958 THE WASHINGTON POST Co.

4/23/58

"Can You See Me Now?"

6/18/57

10

MEANWHILE,
BACK AT THE KREMLIN—

"All Right, Men—Wipe It Off"

"We Play Hot And Sweet"

1/1/56

1/9/56

"Go Back And Tell Them You're A Sovereign State"

12/26/55

3/20/56

"You Can't Tell What Might Come Out Of Those Things"

11/6/55

"This Has Got To Be Decided By Us Germans"

12/6/55

"There's Nothing New Here, But I Just Thought I'd Drop You A Line"

2/5/56

"Now Are There Any Questions?"

2/20/56

"Explain Why You Ain't In There Enjoying The New Freedom, Comrade"

3/21/56

"Poor Old Rip Ivan Winklov—Just Back From 20 Years In Siberia For Having Said Stalin Was A Tyrant"

3/26/56

"Well, What Did You Unlearn Today?"

4/10/56

"Look—I've Rescued You Again"

4/19/56

"Oh-Oh—Hold The Presses Again"

5/11/56

"Look At It This Way—It's Great To Be Alive"

6/6/56

"He Was A Terrible Man, Comrade"

6/1/56

"I've Been Deceived And I'm A Lonesome Little Girl"

6/24/56

"Hey—*Pravda* Is Reprinting From *Us*"

6/29/56

"What Do You Make Of This Rock-'N'-Roll Stuff?"

7/9/56

"You And Your Pal Tito!" "You And Your Pal Stalin!"

11/25/56

"There Are Many Different Paths To Socialism . . ."

12/10/56

"My Death Has Certainly Been Full Of Ups And Downs"

2/25/57

"Well, That's The Way The Ax Bounces"

7/7/57

"Collective Leadership"

7/9/57

Power

7/14/57

"Rise Up!"

8/9/57

Way Down East Russia

9/4/57

Big Squeeze

10/29/57

225

"Now, Panel, What's My Line?"

HERBLOCK
©1957 THE WASHINGTON POST CO.

10/30/57

"You Deviationist!"

6/4/58

The Machine Age

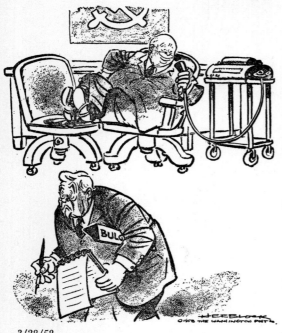

3/28/58

"Trouble Is, There's Too Damn Many Summits Around Here"

4/27/58

"Find Any Fingerprints On It?"

5/13/58

"We Sympathize With Native Aspirations In The Middle East"

8/17/58

11
WORDS, WORDS, WORDS

As a fellow who does drawings, I'm fascinated by words and the wonderful ways in which they are used. Perhaps this goes back to some early story books, profusely illustrated, in which I read of the amazing results achieved by somebody saying, "Sesame!" or "Rumpelstiltskin!" There *is* magic in words—sometimes black magic. Maybe there is in pictures too.

People are always quoting estimates on the comparative values of words and pictures, but I don't think there's any such thing as a fixed ratio. There's supposed to be an old Chinese proverb that one picture is worth ten thousand words—or maybe it's only one thousand words. I felt I was a victim of deflation when an editor once said that one of my drawings was worth a whole paragraph. And my friend Alan Barth insists on quoting an alleged proverb that one word is worth a thousand pictures—which, in his case, may very well be so.

After spending a good part of my life—well, anyhow, what *seems* like a good part of my life—listening to long-winded banquet speakers, the only thing I'm sure of is that there are occasions when one word is worth ten thousand words. And I know what the word is too. It's "goodbye."

But it's the words in political speeches that interest me most. Those are the ones that make me wish I were doing columns instead of cartoons. Each day there are too many events for just one picture. Sometimes a single political speech seems to call for comment in every paragraph. They're often so fully packed with high-sounding but misleading phrases that a guy could devote full time to getting beneath the superficial, without even scratching the surface.

Advertisers and public-relations men have long been telling us of things which they say are needed "now, more than ever." What I think we need now, more than ever, is an ear sharply tuned for what's said—and for what's left unsaid—and a good memory for performance records.

In this era of what might be called The New Demagogy, most politicians have discovered that bombast and oratorical flourishes are as out of date in their line of work as in the theater; and many of them have devoted themselves to the calculated appearance of simple earnestness. Keats may have been right in declaring, "Beauty is truth, truth beauty," but that was before the days of television and public-relations men. Truth and falsehood now look straight into the camera as they read their statements, and you have to guess which one has the phony.

A few men who have done professional television producing for successful politicians have told us that the TV cameras are all-revealing; that people can not be fooled when they see the speakers on the living-room screen. And I wonder why, if this is the case, those same TV directors spend so much time staging these performances, and rehearsing and grooming their charges to get just the right unrehearsed effect. Unfortunately the magic of television, like most magic, seems to depend on careful behind-the-scenes preparation.

A new words-and-pictures combination that has set many people to shaking their heads is subliminal projection—the flashing of words on a motion-picture screen at a rate so rapid that the viewer sees only the movie and is not even conscious of the slogans with which his mind is being bombarded. If this trick can be worked successfully, I'm willing to do as much viewing-with-dismay—and as much nonviewing of TV and movies—as anyone. But the use of such a devious method hardly seems necessary. The same results are already achieved pretty well by the simple repetition of words in plain view or right out loud.

If it is said often enough that officeholder John J. Dokes is the epitome of integrity, a lot of people will accept this as an indisputable fact. And many of them will go on believing it even if he is caught with his hand in the cashbox. Whatever explanation he offers will stand a fair chance of being taken at baby-face value by those who have been conditioned to associate Dokes with honesty and integrity; because after a sufficient buildup, the idea of Dokes taking money *and telling lies besides* will be just too much to grasp.

We all know how winged words like "peace" and "democracy" have been harnessed to pull the chariots of tyrants abroad. But heroic words are also used to draw peddlers' carts and political band wagons at home. *Peace*—it's wonderful! We're all for it. But we can't insure it just by wishing for it, or by putting it on campaign banners. And it makes a difference whether it's peace-with-freedom or, say, peace-with-a-tombstone.

A number of political magic words come readily to mind, as well they

"Forward, Crusaders!"

4/20/56

231

"What *Is* 'Modern,' Anyhow?"

2/15/57

should after beating on our eardrums for so long. One of them is "dedicated," which has had a great vogue in recent years. Jones or Smith, we will hear from the orators, is "a dedicated man." He may be dedicated to feathering his nest, or to disposing of public treasures as fast as he can sign them off to his campaign contributors. But who's going to worry about details like that? Man, he's *dedicated*!

A really noble word and one to set the pennants waving in our hearts is "crusade." There have been men in public life who were indeed crusaders; but too many "crusades" run from nomination to Election Day and are fought to get in from being out. Some of the political propagandists seem to have been fighting a crusade against the English language, by using this word to describe campaigns for re-election. How can you "crusade" to keep your job, sit tight, and maintain the status quo? Don't be standing around asking questions, bub. Here comes the parade.

A candidate who is *a dedicated man*, of great *integrity*, and who conducts a successful campaign *crusade*, is certainly going to come up with a *program*. Maybe several of them. There is no limit to the amount an official—or his speech writers—can produce, because all that is required is some numbers and the announcement that a program is being offered. The rest can consist of a procession of duck-billed platitudes or even pages from the phone book. It won't make any difference, particularly if it is set in type properly. Thus:

1 For the money spent in taxes, the people should receive value.

2 For the show of honest intentions there can be no substitute.

3 To get ready for possible emergencies is the duty of our armed forces.

4 To go forward, ever forward, must be our aim.

The above paragraphs do not constitute much of anything but an expanded version of the old jingle, "One for the money, two for the show, three to get ready, and four to go." But if they are properly launched in a speech, and if they appear in type under a heading, ZILCH PRESENTS FOUR-POINT PROGRAM, they will do nicely. They will be considered a "program" until they are forgotten and another four-, eight-, twelve-, or umpteen-point program is unfurled.

Of all the fine words that have been dragged, tired and begging for mercy, through political speeches, one of the saddest is "dignity." We hear that this or that man will bring, or has brought, *dignity* to high office. That one had me puzzled for a while, but after studying some of the men eulogized in this way, I figured it out. Dignity means wearing a vest.

There was a time, in the old days, when it was said that there was dignity in honest toil. There was dignity in the expression of great thoughts. There was a dignity in public office that was above the acceptance of valuable personal gifts. There was dignity in rolling up the sleeves and fighting for great causes.

But public-relations politics, shrewdly recognizing that in wooing voters it's the *little* things that count, has simplified everything. It has made dignity as easily recognizable as the nearest headwaiter, correctly attired and with the proper nod or smile at the right time. And dignified officeholders certainly must not be guilty of using profane words in public. For example, where special interests are concerned it's bad taste to give 'em hell, but okay to give 'em Hells Canyon.

By way of illustrating this simple thought, let me set down here, where they can find a place to rest, a couple of homemade editorials I once used in a journalism lecture.

They are not professional pieces. They are just some things I constructed for my own amusement during the period when do-it-yourself projects were all the rage. I started with a good, solid, standard item that I had seen many times in many forms, and which I had come to think of as The Truman Editorial:

Wet Blanket

The nation has once been more treated to the unedifying spectacle of a former President of the United States shooting off his mouth in a rash, ill-timed remark characterized by unbridled partisanship and profanity.

When reporters accosted Mr. Truman on his morning stroll yesterday, they inquired what he thought of the weather. In his cockiest, shooting-from-the-hip manner, Mr. Truman told the astonished group, "Boys, I think it's going to rain like hell."

The Missouri politician could hardly have been unaware of the fact that his intemperate statement ran directly counter to the official weather forecast, which was Clear and Sunny. He was, in effect, casting aspersions upon the present Administration, under which the Weather Bureau operates, and, indeed, upon the Press, which faithfully published the Bureau's forecast.

His words were apparently calculated to spread gloom and promote panic among the thousands who planned picnics and other

"Dam! Dam! Triple Dam!"

6/9/57

outdoor diversions, and to lessen public confidence in the judgment of the President, who was already on his way to the golf course. We can well imagine the glee with which the masters of the Kremlin must have greeted this latest attempt to create division and sow disunity among Americans.

To be sure, we did have some fourteen inches of rain yesterday. But to belabor that coincidence would be to miss the essential point of the matter. Mr. Truman is not an authorized weather prognosticator and, in fact, he no longer holds any public position whatsoever. Furthermore, nobody is interested in what private-citizen Truman thinks; and the next time we send our reporters to interview him we hope he will have the good grace to remember that.

In the other editorial I thought I'd try something a little different and put together a piece on government:

Clearing the Air

By now most of our readers are probably aware of the current to-do over the Washington Monument. As a result of a transaction—which was reported in the St. Louis *Post-Dispatch* two months ago and verified by the wire services last week—the Washington Monument has now been dismantled and shipped to a gentleman in Texas, who is having it reconstructed, at no cost to the taxpayers, as a stone oil derrick.

As might have been expected, partisans in Congress have been quick to raise the cry of "giveaway"—despite the fact that the Texan paid $55 for the structure, as he agreed to do when the purchase was made. The simple fact is that a formerly idle monument is now being put to constructive use and has been converted from a government liability to a Treasury asset which will help to balance the budget.

Whatever misunderstandings might have been occasioned by this transaction were cleared up at yesterday's White House press conference. Here the President said, in direct answer to correspondents' questions, that he obviously could not keep track of all the monuments in the country, but that this he would tell them: That he had the highest respect for George Washington; that he thought it would be unfortunate if anyone sought to drag the name of Washington into what was essentially a political controversy; and that if any reporters wanted to know about the legal aspects of the monument removal he felt sure that Attorney General Brownell would eventually see them.

This frank and forthright statement by the President should put an end to rumors and reckless charges concerning a perfectly proper and highly desirable transaction.

However, this newspaper does feel that there is some validity to criticisms of the manner in which the transaction became public. It is always the occasion of some confusion when one newspaper obtains a "scoop" in a matter of this kind; and we feel it would be well if the White House staff co-ordinated its work in such a way that stories of future monument-removal transactions were mimeographed and released promptly to all accredited correspondents.

Time moves on, and so do some of the government figures whose names were large in the news just a short time ago. To avoid operating a shuttle between these lines and footnotes, I might as well mention here that when the Attorney General mentioned above resigned in October 1957, he had not held a press conference for two years.

Fashions in words also have a way of changing, as is known to anyone who has stumbled through some Elizabethan literature or even listened to youthful slang for a few months. Some words and phrases reach a crest in popularity, when they come easily to the lips and roll naturally off the typewriters. Then, suddenly, they will be discarded, to be used only at the risk of seeming hopelessly old hat.

Popular words of one decade, like *scandal* and *corruption*, become in another decade *conflicts-of-interest, imprudences,* and *disservices to our President.* Likewise, *criticism of the Administration* may become *personal attacks on the President*; and *demands for official cleanup* may become *attacks on the United States Government.*

The general tendency in recent years has been toward more genteel words. But there are exceptions. In the Senate investigation of labor racketeering, words like *crook* and *corruption* were tossed about with all the old-time vigor. This was perfectly all right because just about everyone—including responsible labor-union officials—was in agreement on that usage. However, it would not have been good form to have pointed out that a top teamster-union official, designated as a crook, had been entertained by our very highest officials and had contributed to their campaigns. That would have been unseemly.

If Theodore Roosevelt had been around when the Snake River dam site, which he set aside for the people, was handed over to private power interests, he might have shouted about "malefactors of great wealth," political "weasel words" or worse. If this trust-buster had heard about the Department of Justice busting up antitrust suits begun under a previous Administration, he might have applied a big stick to the men in that branch of government. And if he had heard about wildlife refuges and timberlands being handed

Belshazzar's Feast

5/1/56

"Who—Me?"

3/28/57

"I'd Letcha Have A Coupla Hunnert Grand Till Pay Day But I Just Mislaid A Few Hunnert Grand"

3/25/57

"What Are You Going To Do About It, Chum?"

10/6/57

238

"Ah, Yes—We Must Look After Our Little Four-Wheeled Friends"

12/29/55

"You Say You Have This Impression That You Keep Smelling Oil?"

4/29/57

over to private interests for exploitation, he probably would have cut loose with a bull-moose bellow that could have been heard throughout the entire land. He might not have understood all the delicate nuances of "dynamic conservatism." And instead of being called a square dealer he might be considered just a square.

A fellow like that would be out of touch with things. The political press agents and speech writers would have to explain to him the difference between a gift (which is a token of esteem) and a bribe. They would also have to explain to him the difference between cronyism (which is ugly) and friendship (which is a sweet and lovely thing).

They could explain those delicate distinctions because they are very gifted men, though evidently not quite as gifted as some of the officials they serve.

The fine meanings of words like "friendship" and "gifts" and the full flowering of public-relations morality in government were brought to public attention during the Congressional investigation of federal regulatory agencies in 1958. In the early stages of this investigation it developed that some members of the Federal Communications Commission had received tele-

"You Fellows Go Right On Talking—I'll Let You Know When I Reach a Decision"

5/26/58

vision sets and occasional travel expenses—sometimes, inadvertently, *double* travel expenses—from members of the industry they were regulating.

The investigation warmed up when it was shown that one FCC commissioner had for years received financial assistance from an old friend, who in later years had been interested in some of the cases under FCC jurisdiction. With some urging from the Congressional committee, the commissioner submitted his resignation. This was promptly snapped up by the President, who felt that the FCC member was doing the right thing in removing himself from office.

The committee discovered so much jockeying around and so many calls from men of influence that its counsel was moved to say, "It would appear that the ex parte pressure was more responsible for the [FCC] decisions than the announced standards for the decisions themselves . . ."

Ah, the magic of words! A few words here, a few words there—from the right people—and, presto!—difficult decisions are made easy.

Among the many interesting sidelights of the investigation was the testimony of the friend of an unsuccessful applicant for a TV channel in Miami. This friend had spoken with a friend of *his*, who was described as an intimate golfing companion of the President and a friend of many Congressmen. The result of these conversations was that the applicant's friend relayed to him the opinion of the friend-of-big-wheels that the FCC license would be bestowed upon someone else, and "naturally it would be a Republican." The opinion turned out to be correct.

The communications with which the FCC dealt seemed to include not only wireless but mental telepathy. In some cases, the right people knew what the commission's decision would be months in advance of the announcement. In one disputed case, an applicant proceeded to buy his broadcasting-station equipment long before he was awarded his license. How subtle can communications get?

The real excitement in this investigation began when it was disclosed that Sherman Adams, the Assistant to the President, had got in touch with members of federal regulatory agencies to make inquiries on behalf of friends.

Interest reached a pitch when it developed that Mr. Adams had received from an old friend—who happened to have dealings and difficulties with federal regulatory commissions—such tokens of esteem as a $600 vicuña coat, over $3,000 worth of hotel expenses, and a $2,400 carpet—all of which the friend had chalked up to tax-deductible business expenses.

Mr. Adams explained that the carpet which his friend had purchased specifically for the Adams floor was only a loan, to be returned after he had worn it down for a few years. Alas for history that the words of that extravagant but not too generous arrangement went unrecorded. I've often wondered just how it could have been phrased.

Mr. Adams, who had, a few years earlier, screamed as loudly as anyone about a mink coat and a few deep freezes, seemed somewhat baffled that anyone might think him guilty of anything more than modest "imprudence." He must have been even more baffled when he recalled the tens of thousands of dollars' worth of personal gifts that had been accepted by his "superior officer," as he referred to the President. These included horses, hogs, a herd of cattle, a $3,000 putting green, a $1,000 farm runabout and a $4,000 tractor, among many other items that could hardly be turned over to museums.

The matter of gifts, as the President had explained on an earlier occasion when a comparatively minor official was involved, was a matter of taste. There's probably nothing less tasteful than a couple of naked deep freezes or fur coats without a few classy appurtenances to go with them—especially if such simple gifts are received by members of the opposition party. Booty is in the eye of the beholder. Or perhaps I should say beauty is in the eye of the beholden.

In Sherman Adams' testimony to the Congressional committee, it developed that even he, who had turned out some of the most self-righteous speeches of recent years, was not entirely conscious of the magic of words. He didn't quite seem to understand how a call from the White House to federal commission members—whose appointments and reappointments depended on White House approval—might carry any more weight than a call from anyone else.

This modesty was very touching, and it also made me feel better about my own failure to appreciate some of the fine words that had been spread around in public speeches.

Probably the saddest words since "It might have been" were those which the President uttered at a press conference following the Adams disclosures, when he said plaintively, "I need him."

At the same time, some publications, even while frowning at the Adams "imprudences," continued to point out that he was obviously a man of the greatest "probity" and "rectitude." In connection with the idea of Sherman Adams being involved in any hanky-panky one word that had been used was "unthinkable." And, in a way, this was apt.

But why was it "unthinkable" in the case of Sherman Adams and perfectly "thinkable" in the case of a couple of lesser officials in the previous Administration who had been officially clobbered and even sent to jail for conduct no more questionable? It was because of what we had consistently heard and read.

How could anyone think of calling a sponge a sponge if he had always heard it called a New Hampshire granite rock? The magic of words again; it was all done with mirrors, endlessly reflecting a few phrases.

"The Advertising Sounded Great"

6/15/58

"There's A Small Hotel
With A Wishing Well"

6/12/58

244

6/18/58

6/19/58

Perhaps it's only coincidence that officials who are not quite honest with the people sometimes also become involved in "imprudences" involving money and gifts. But if so, the coincidences are lucky ones; because at times nothing less than a fur coat or a carpet or cash on the line seems tangible enough to outweigh press releases.

There was some debate as to whether the Assistant to the President was "corruptible." But I think that word missed the main point. The question was whether he and his associates were corrupt*ing*. If nonpolitical jobs are cleared through a party organization; if party contributions influence the award of government contracts; if the Justice Department is more zealous in prosecuting members of one political party than those of another—or in prosecuting small firms than big businesses; if the federal regulatory agencies are stacked with men whose decisions are not based on the public interest—then our government has been corrupted.

No coats or carpets or other gifts should be necessary to spell things out; and they are a small matter compared to the corruption of government itself. If the wrong men are selected to serve on supposedly independent commissions, it's hardly even necessary that phone calls be made to them. There are cases where words are superfluous. As somebody once said, "the milk-wagon horse knows where to stop."

In 1958 some newspapers recalled the speeches of the 1952 campaign, when General Eisenhower had said that unworthy men would not even get *into* an Administration of his; and when he had promised that he would bring to Washington the best brains and men of the highest standing.

Those words about the best brains reminded me of something. In *Alice In Wonderland* the March Hare had oiled the watch with butter and gummed up the works. "It was the *best* butter," he sadly told the Hatter.

There had been brought into the machinery of government the best butter-uppers, men who knew which side their bread was buttered on, and men in whose mouths butter wouldn't melt. And, as the Hatter grumbled to the March Hare, "some crumbs must have got in."

Who would try to improve on the words of Lewis Carroll?

"Timber! Oops—I Mean 'Mineral Research!' "

HERBLOCK
©1956 THE WASHINGTON POST CO

1/20/56

"We Don't Want You To Feel Left Out Of This"

5/1/57

"It's Real Private Enterprise—He Takes Your Money To The Bank All By Himself"

5/17/57

"I Thought You Said You Finished Him This Time"

7/12/57

"I Don't Want Anything More About That"

2/28/58

248

"Too Bad You Ain't A Power Company, Kid"

HERBLOCK
©1957 THE WASHINGTON POST CO.

7/24/57

"They Act As If They've Been Doped"

8/5/57

250

"Why, Yes—I Agree With You Completely"

7/18/55

"You Must Tell Me About Your Work Sometime, Dear"

1/11/57

"I've Got My Hands On The Reins All The Time"

1/31/58

"A Thousand Apologies, Gentlemen. He's A New Man"

2/9/58

"It Looks As If Somebody Had Pay TV"

2/14/58

"Okay—Keep At It"

3/6/58

"All I Got Was One Station In Florida"

4/30/58

"I Think We're Beginning To Get The Picture"

6/21/58

2/20/58

"What! My Administration Influenced By Money?"

8/2/57

"By The Way, Who Appoints Those Fellows?"

2/26/58

"We Want To Send A Big Man There. Let's See—"

3/24/57

"Very Good—Put That Man At The Head Of The Class"

7/31/57

"Say, What Ever Happened To That Crusade, Anyhow?"

HERBLOCK
©1955 THE WASHINGTON POST CO.

10/31/55

About the Author

HERBERT BLOCK, or Herblock, of Washington, D. C., has been a professional cartoonist for twenty-nine years. He was born in Chicago in 1909. At the age of 19 he left Lake Forest College to become the editorial-page cartoonist for the Chicago *Daily News*. Then came the NEA newspaper feature service in Cleveland, the Army, and the *Washington Post* (now the *Washington Post and Times Herald*), where he has been since 1946. Today his cartoons, distributed by the Hall Syndicate, appear in 200 papers from Washington to Bangkok—including *The Manchester Guardian* and *The London Economist*.

Mr. Block has been awarded the Pulitzer Prize (twice), the American Newspaper Guild Award, the Heywood Broun Award, the *Parents Magazine* Award for outstanding service to education, four awards from Sigma Delta Chi, the national journalism society—and two from the National Cartoonists Society: in 1957 the Cartoonist of the Year Award and, in 1958, the Best Editorial Cartoonist Award.

In 1950 the State Department published a pamphlet of Mr. Block's cartoons, *Herblock Looks at Communism,* for use overseas. More than a million copies have been distributed.

Herblock's Special for Today is Mr. Block's third book. He is the author of *The Herblock Book* (winner of the Sidney Hillman Award for nonfiction) and *Herblock's Here and Now.*